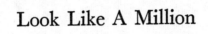
Look Like A Million

Look Like A Million

❧❧❧

Leslie Field

Illustrations by Lucy Su

HART-DAVIS, MACGIBBON
GRANADA PUBLISHING
London Toronto Sydney New York

Published by Granada Publishing in
Hart-Davis, MacGibbon Ltd 1978

Granada Publishing Limited
Frogmore, St Albans, Herts AL2 2NF
and
3 Upper James Street, London W1R 4BP
1221 Avenue of the Americas, New York, NY 10020, USA
117 York Street, Sydney, NSW 2000, Australia
100 Skyway Avenue, Toronto, Ontario, Canada M9W 3A6
Trio City, Coventry Street, Johannesburg 2001, South Africa
CML Centre, Queen & Wyndham, Auckland 1, New Zealand

Copyright © Leslie Field 1978

ISBN 0 246 11043 0

Printed in Great Britain by
Richard Clay (The Chaucer Press) Ltd
Bungay, Suffolk

Contents

FOR PATRICK

I ✿ Introduction

I don't have classically beautiful features; my body has as much wrong as right with it; and I wasn't born rich enough to substitute cash for style, but ever since I can first remember I've adored clothes and that passion has made me a magazine and newspaper editor, a radio pundit and television presenter.

At twenty I got my first job in the New York fashion industry as the *Vogue* magazine receptionist, and since then I have learned a million tricks of the trade; so that now I can go anywhere and do anything, knowing I look my best. And if I can do it, you can do it!

In the thirteen years since that very first job interview at Condé Nast Publications, I've been a Fashion Editor at *Glamour*; Fashion and Fabric Editor at *Ingénue*; feature writer on newspapers like *The Times*, the *Daily Mail*, and the *Daily Express*; and now I'm the Editor of the *Tatler*.

Two years after moving to London from New York City, I became the Fashion Editor of the *Sunday Times*, and each week I tried to create and write a page that not only informed readers what was going on in the fashion world but also pinpointed international trends in High Street styles.

In 1974 I started a programme called 'The Passionate Shopper' on London's LBC Radio, and then in 1975 I went to Capital Radio where, on the morning Michael Aspel Show I reported on fashion and beauty; and on the evening London Today programme I gave tips on sales and shopping for special occasions.

It was *Glamour* magazine in the mid-sixties that originally sparked off my interest in the 'How To's' of fashion, but it was

7

my post bag at the *Sunday Times* that convinced me that every woman is seeking the self-confidence that being well dressed brings – and most of us don't know whom to turn to for help.

I've written this book for all the women like me – who have too little time, and too little money – side by side with an overwhelming desire to look our best. I discuss what you must spend money on and where you can cheat, what to put on your face, how to improve your body, how to save at sales, and what is a once-in-a-lifetime investment.

Whatever city you live in, the mechanics of being well dressed remain the same, and status symbols are international. I am a great believer in Investment Shopping, and fashion tricks have taken me from Buckingham Palace to the White House.

I've got all the insecurities of other women, if not more – considering the beautiful females I work with. But knowing the shortcuts, knowing what looks good and is appropriate anywhere in the world, I've now got enough self-confidence to meet anyone. I've been lucky enough to have learnt my tricks from some of the most knowledgeable and elegant women in the world.

I do the best I can to make the most of my good points, and then forget about the rest. 'What the eye doesn't see, the heart doesn't grieve over' is very true; and feeling inferior isn't the worst thing in the world if it makes me try harder.

When I wake up in the morning I'm a brown-haired, medium-sized lady. Nothing fabulous about me at all, quite ordinary in fact; but by the time I've spent fifteen minutes on my make-up, and dressed to face the world, I know I can make anyone I pass on the street give me a second look. And there isn't a woman alive who can't do it just as well as me.

Beauty doesn't lie in the eye of the beholder, it's only reflected there; which is why looking beautiful gives you pleasure. Beauty is a serious business, you can make more of your life by making more of yourself.

Luckily there is no such thing as perfect beauty; and beauty is being true to one's type. Making defects work for you, however, is a difficult art and one at which all of us can do with some professional help.

Most women have faults they need to camouflage or eliminate, rather than emphasize. When I think back to the beauties I've met, they've all arrived at a very personal style by eliminating anything that doesn't work for them. When I look in the mirror I don't say, 'oh good', I say 'oh-oh', and start plotting to improve the situation.

This book is all about giving yourself a new look. A new figure, new face, and new self-confidence, with which to face the world. It's a very personal book; I made myself over, and I think you should too.

Starting today, right now, this very minute, make a commitment to yourself to do whatever it takes to look better. Can you think of anything more worthwhile?

2 ❧ Making The Most Of Yourself

First Impressions

Everything about your face, your hair, your clothes, must all be directed towards only one object. The first impression. Make sure you're one of the handful of people with an extra-special glittery glow who'll stand out in any crowd.

Being dowdy and dull is unforgivable. If you care enough to look your very best you'll get better jobs, meet more attractive men, and have a better time. Really, I promise you. Your looks are the key to open every door.

I know myself; I know my strengths and my weaknesses; and I am willing to take whatever time is needed to show you my good points. What I hate I change, what I can't change I camouflage, and what I can't camouflage I ignore.

You may be one of the millions of women who are attractive but don't show themselves off to their best advantage. I think that women who look good should be admired, and there's nothing that says you shouldn't do everything in your power to improve what you started with. Do the best with what you have. Nothing is for everybody, but I've never met a woman who didn't have at least one feature to accentuate and show off. Walking down a Paris street, I often think the French are better at this than anyone else.

I'm not just being a glib journalist; I made it for years earning about £20 a week and, after I'd paid the rent, there wasn't much left over. It's not how much you spend, it's how much you care.

When do you wash your hair? The day before it really needs it, or the day after, when you've had to hide it under a headscarf? When do you sew back the button on your jacket? The first minute you can lay your hands on needle and thread, or after you've worn it hanging open for a week? When do you check and see if your eyebrows need to be plucked? Last night before you went to bed, or in the Ladies during coffee break this morning. When you bump into Mr Right on the street, can you concentrate on admiring his blue eyes? Or are you too busy worrying about your pinned-up hem?

Any woman who doesn't look great just doesn't want to. You must do whatever works best for you, and the only way to begin is begin. The sooner you start, the sooner you'll see results. How do you know there's anything in life that isn't right for you if you don't try it? First experiment, then say 'yuck'. There are moments in life for which everything that has gone before seems a preparation. Fantasize a little; if the genie came out of the bottle right this minute, what would you want to be?

There may be lots of things in this book that won't apply to you, but I hope there'll also be things that spur you on to rethink your looks and any problems that you thought were insurmountable. What I've put down are the things I've discovered that do or don't work for me, and I speak from experience as I've tried them all.

Change

Never say 'never': open up to new ideas as they sail into view. Yes, of course decide you don't like something, but don't decide until you've given it a try. The quickest way to grow old mentally and physically is to be inflexible.

Toss out all the old rules you've been taught about dressing and spend ten seconds on anything new saying 'how would it look?' I hope that by the time you've finished reading this book all sorts of new ideas will have sprung at you, and there'll be half a dozen things you try right away. Once you've developed a sense of yourself you'll be able to adapt any new idea that comes along to suit you.

Looking contemporary and up to date reflects an optimistic

approach to life. 'Dated' is such a sad insult, because so unnecessary. Once you're looking terrific there's the temptation to
stay just as you are, but getting into a rut is instant death and I
expect you to resist it every step of the way.

Life is never settled. It is crammed full of endless choices;
perpetual new discoveries; constant re-evaluation. One of the
most fabulous words in our vocabulary is 'yes'. Yes, I'm open to
experience, open to life, open to pleasure, and even sometimes to
being hurt; but whatever the outcome, at least I never said, 'No,
I'm afraid to try.' Boots, a fringe, long red fingernails, a twenty-
five-inch waist are all things I have today that I didn't three
years ago.

The first rule about change is that it demands a constant re-
ordering of one's concept of oneself. I used to see myself as a sweet
'Alice in Wonderland' figure – bright eyes, blushing cheeks,
blowing locks tied back with a band; but then my thirtieth birthday loomed, a perfect ceremonial date on which to rearrange my
priorities. Shorn was the hair, changed was the make-up, mix and
match played with the clothes in the cupboard: and suddenly I
was a gamine and sometimes glamorous woman, no longer an
over-age nymphet.

The biggest enemy of change is Procrastination. Don't put
things off. Start today, after all it is the first day of the rest of your
life.

Mrs Vreeland

I've always been strongly influenced by women I admire, and
when your taste is still unsure and untried, finding someone to
emulate is the best thing that can happen to you.

When I started to work at *Vogue*, the Editor was Diana Vreeland, and watching her over the months I was stationed at the
front desk taught me lots of things. If I had been less self-conscious
and inhibited, I would have learned even more, but in those days
I wanted to be safe, more than I dreamed of being sensational.

Today, Mrs Vreeland has become a legendary figure; as
Special Consultant to The Metropolitan Museum of Art, she has
been staging costume exhibitions that attract hundreds of
thousands of people.

Look Like A Million

At *Vogue*, she used to arrive at the office about 11.30 a.m. Jet black hair pulled severely back from her high forehead, and a most particular loping walk; her feet, in impeccably crafted T-strap low-heeled pumps, were placed down very precisely; first toe, then heel, as if they came in two separate pieces.

She never failed to wave and say good morning as she went through a door at the opposite end of the corridor. Two of her three secretaries became friends, and when I would stop by for a gossip I would catch a glimpse of Mrs Vreeland's Chinese lacquer red office, her trademark colour; and it inspired me to paint my 2 by 3-foot kitchen the same spectacular shade when I got my first flat later that year.

Mrs Vreeland didn't seem to have a lot of clothes, or at least I saw her in the same double-breasted woollen coat nearly every day. In a Christmas sale I found a black coat cut exactly like hers, so I knew it had to be right; and when she wound a fur boa around the collar, I did a trade with my mother and wore hers, day in and day out, at exactly the same angle.

This was the era of stiletto heels and pointed toes, and I'd never even seen the low-heeled chunky Gucci moccasin until Mrs V. announced it was the only shoe to wear; and thirteen years later I still have my bamboo handled leather handbag because she said it was elegant.

There must have been thousands of girls like me, in her forty years of fashion influence, who had their eyes opened to the beauty of originality and simplicity by this remarkable woman. She made me re-evaluate what I thought of as beauty; droves of models would arrive to see her, but her favourites, Verushka, Marisa Berenson, Penelope Tree, constantly reappearing, weren't conventionally pretty, and I didn't understand their looks nearly as well as the blonde Grace Kelly types.

Mrs Vreeland was married to one of the most charming and distinguished looking men I've ever met, and once at a dance I plucked up my courage to tell him how awed I was by his wife, and he laughed, and kindly told me to just do my job and not worry about her. She inspired ambition in me because I wanted to get closer to her fascinating orbit.

Simplicity

My code of living is to simplify everything. You don't have to wear expensive clothes or jewellery to be alluring – it's all in your attitude. Simplicity is godliness when it comes to fashion; err on the side of understatement. Simplicity doesn't mean poverty, it's just that less is more. Strive for uncluttered lines, no fuss, easy sophistication. To stand out in a crowd, underwhelm people.

It's a very old maxim that still works; once you're completely dressed, stand in front of the mirror, examine yourself carefully, and take just one thing off.

Discipline

By temperament, I am unutterably lazy, but at the same time I'm very beauty conscious. My body goes to flab in the blink of an eye, so I force myself to the discipline of exercise classes. If I so much as look at food it's gone to my hips, so day in and day out, everything I don't eat is spartan self-denial.

Washing my hair, painting my nails, getting my legs waxed; they all take time, and none is much fun, but discipline makes such beauty habits automatic. Then I am free to learn the tricks and flourishes that will give me dazzle and make me glamorous.

Facing the world is like building a house; until the basement is down, the walls up, the floorboards covered, I can't begin the decorating, which is the amusing part. Anything I do to look better is done as simply and quickly as possible. The only consolation about discipline is that the things you do are for your own good. The pleasure in the end result makes the effort worthwhile.

Choosing your Type

I like to think I have *style*. The secret of style is that if you have enough of it, other people pick it up by osmosis and imagine that with your fashion savvy, even your mistakes are right. Style is to a certain extent instinctive, a flair you're born with. Good taste can be bought, but style you possess. If you're poor with style, there's sure to be a millionaire waiting around some turning, but if you're rich with style, then the world's your oyster.

Look Like A Million

Style depends on character and it can take time to evolve, but the fascinating thing about it is its elusiveness. It's glamorous, irresistible, and should dazzle the eye of the beholder.

Find your own style. I may hate it, but Janet Street Porter with her green hair has style; Zandra Rhodes charging £300 for punk rock dresses needs style; Bianca Jagger in her men's suits has it even when it shocks; and Princess Alexandra dresses the way most of us really want to, stylishly safe, and that's style too.

I don't mind admitting that I copy people, and things; I don't borrow but steal, and in the end I make it mine. Everything, whether it's a scarf, a hair-do, make-up, a brooch, or a hat, can be worn in a variety of ways. Take the best from everyone, but then wear it so well that everyone else wants to steal it from you.

Chic is another component of style and it's nearly impossible to pin down. Why does one girl wear an inexpensive dress with such an air that it looks as if she's walking down an invisible red carpet, and next to her a dreary lady is wearing mink as if it were rabbit?

Chic women have to be covered to look their best, they rarely have beautiful bodies and look terrible naked. It's hard to wear elegant clothes perfectly if you're built like Diana Dors because you bulge too much and spoil the line of the garment. A woman with a mediocre figure can, if she wears clothes with an air, artfully drapes a shawl, stylishly ties a scarf, and walks as if she's got on the Crown Jewels, give the illusion of chic.

A very good word is *flair*, which the French say means 'a nose that instinctively senses the right thing'. Glamour is good packaging, and a fabulous word I learned at *Vogue* is *pazazz*, which is 'an unknown essential of fashion meaning jazzy, only more so'. If you ever saw the film *Funny Face* about the behind-the-scenes world of a fashion magazine, you'll have heard it then.

Elegance has more to do with perfectionism and self-discipline. You can be poor and still have style, but the upkeep on elegance takes a certain amount of financial security. It's elegant to know that something is as beautiful on the wrong side as on the right.

Elegance is pearly teeth, manicured fingernails, silk lingerie, linen sheets, alligator handbags. It's never looking rumpled or having your lipstick smeared. It's got magic; you look a certain way, but no one knows why you do or what's going on to make it happen.

16

I've decided to wait till I'm forty, and then I'm going to start worrying about whether I'm elegant or not.

Money and Taste

When I was twenty and began work at *Vogue*, I was greatly in awe of the glamorous ladies wafting around, but after five months I transferred to *Vogue*'s sister publication *Glamour*, where I was secretary to the Shoe Editor, and here I felt immediately at home, for its slogan was 'More Taste Than Money', which is exactly how I fancied my own style.

Of course it's easy to look good if you've got unlimited cash; you just waltz into Yves St Laurent or Jap, and buy whatever the designer dictates is this season's look. But a real dress sense doesn't depend on how much money you have.

Having taste is being imaginative and combining lots of things and making them all look good. The combination of poverty and no imagination is deadly. Money gives you access to people who can substitute their taste for the lack of yours. Many very rich women have no style at all – but they manage to get it all together because they hire help.

I think there's something creative about a woman who is well put together. It matters less what you begin with than what you do with what you have. If you spend the time, and have the flair, you can look just as good on a tight budget as Jackie Kennedy Onassis does with all her millions.

Taste is far more important than money – as long as your body is in good shape, your skin clear, your hair shiny, you can be well dressed for surprisingly little outlay. Taste is very personal and individual. Always watch what others are doing; windowshop; look at all the fashion magazines; analyse the displays in expensive stores; notice how things are being put together this season, and what colours work well together. Then make your own choices.

To be well dressed, you have to be so continuously, not in fits and starts. That doesn't mean you can't have lots of different looks: sportif in the morning, demure at lunch, fragile in drifting skirts at night. But be cohesive, be perfect all the time.

If you've ever spent ten minutes browsing through a good jeweller's you'll know that possessing gold is not always synonymous with good taste. Many of the world's biggest spenders, some of whom even end up on Best Dressed Lists, are badly dressed. The BDL, as it's known in the fashion trade, is compiled by a small group of powerful public relations experts and journalists; if you're a client of the one, you end up in the column of the other, and if you spend enough money in the salons of fellow clients, who happen to be fashion designers, you're probably going to end up on the list. In other words, expenditure in the right places, and *voilà*, you're on the Best Dressed List.

Fashion Magazines

The best, easiest and cheapest way to keep abreast of the latest fashion trends is to look at every fashion magazine and newspaper you can lay your hands on. Aside from getting your eye in about new proportions and new looks, you'll also get ideas on new ways to put things together. Many of the bits and pieces may already be gathering dust in your cupboard, and you'll suddenly see a different way in which to wear them. Work out new colour combinations; different ways to tie scarves; how to drape a shawl; all things you can learn by looking.

Since I don't normally buy high fashion clothes; since I don't replace my wardrobe every season; and since my taste is more cautious than the latest issue of *Vogue*, lots of what I see I dislike; but six months from now, when a fashion trend hits the chain stores, I'll understand it and I'll know where it sifted down from.

The most obvious place to look at all the new magazines is at the hairdresser's. If you get there only once a month, arrive early for your appointment and grab all the latest glossies; if that's not on, make a monthly stop at your local library. Because of my job I have to read everything, and then I pass them on to friends, figuring that such circulation at least cuts the cover price, and chums are delighted to have me stay as a houseguest, since I come like a Greek bearing gifts. Band together with four friends, share the cost, and you'll all know the latest looks.

The hardest thing to learn is not to react too quickly. Because it's unknown, don't automatically say, 'I could never wear that'; why not an adaptation of it, or some part of it? Using the magazines as a reference point can also help you decide the way you don't want to look.

A good fashion page tells you how to wear the clothes, when to wear them and where to wear them. Never worry about price tags; you're not buying these specific clothes, just developing your own taste. Think about what you see; does it suit you now, or if you cut your hair, lost weight, changed your make-up, how would it look then?

Even more important than clothes, the glossies are a Do-It-Yourself guide to hair and make-up. Three or four times a year the best beauty companies such as Revlon, Rubinstein, and Lauder bring out new make-up stories, and beautifully made-up models can be used as examples for any of us. The mouth is bow shaped, is it? The shading around the eyes goes up at the corners, does it? The moons are being left bare on fingernails this winter, are they?

Train your eye – that's what counts. Let nothing get past you.

Status Symbols

Status symbols are pearls above price, for they get you better tables in restaurants, quicker service in shops and more attention from attractive business magnates in aeroplanes. 'The rich are not like you and me', said F. Scott Fitzgerald; and the more I see of them, the more I agree, but it's reassuring to know that one can look like them just by buying in the same stores.

Status symbols are established overnight if all the 'right people' are suddenly sporting it, but often enough it's been around for ages. In the 1920s the chic set travelled with Louis Vuitton cases, but it was the advent of jet travel, and the need for lightweight luggage, that made them an international necessity. Now of course the clever have given them up, because Customs officers have cottoned on to what they cost.

I've always coveted status symbols, but it was my years as a New York fashion editor that made them sacrosanct in my eyes. In the mid-sixties there was a recognizable look prevalent in the land. As exemplified by Jackie Kennedy, the simplicity of fashion editor taste had swept the country by teaching the high fashion mathematics of multiplying chic by subtraction. In 1964 status symbols proclaimed, 'I am rich, I am well connected, I know what's what.'

The seventies' recession hasn't abolished status, it has merely reversed it. Now it's no longer how much one has paid for something, but how little.

Status symbols are the ultimate in camouflage dressing: have on at least one instantly recognizable item and it won't occur to anyone that everything else isn't as high calibre.

SS's are often expensive, that's part of the point of them, but they have an unlimited life span. Get yourself any of the following and you can't go wrong.

Gucci moccasins with a tiny brass bit as in a horse's harness across the front. Get a new pair in the sale every year, either black or brown, patent or pigskin. As of writing, the two pairs I currently wear are brown pigskins from 1973 and black patent from 1975. I reckon each pair is good for three years of hard wear, and the scruffier they get the more chic they are.

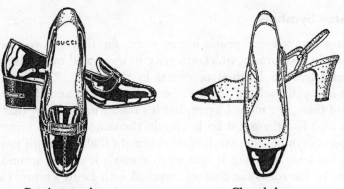

Gucci moccasins   Chanel shoe

Chanel beige and black sling-back pumps. Probably the sexiest shoe ever designed; it shows off the legs to perfection and is cut away at the top of the toes for a small erotic touch. Perfect for wearing with dinner dresses, and adds an air of French chic to a simple skirt and shirt. They look equally good at night with trousers and a silk shirt.

Cartier rolling ring; the traditional Russian wedding ring. Three skinny bands, yellow, pink and white gold; looped through each other, hence the name 'rolling ring'. Very 'in' to wear it on the little finger; a favourite with royalty going back to the late Duke of Windsor. Not expensive and widely copied.

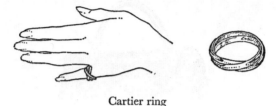

Cartier ring

Cartier Tank Watch. Designed in 1917 by Louis Cartier, the classic design hasn't changed one iota. The special bracelet clasp is recognized by the *cognoscenti* everywhere, even with the face copied as often as it is. In this case, imitation is definitely the sincerest form of flattery.

Cartier watch

Hermès Kelly handbag, named after Grace Kelly. These large satchels haven't changed by a stitch in at least thirty years. Indispensable to the elegant woman travelling in the days of leisurely ocean crossings, the double straps and padlock closing offered extra security for valuables. I find it fabulous for both travelling and working. I have the larger of two sizes, and it can hold not only the normal contents of a handbag but also, when needed: book, notepad, Pentax camera, pens, film, etc, yet it always looks graceful and not in the least like a suitcase. On the three occasions I've gone to Buckingham Palace to interview

Prince Philip I've carried it, and all my equipment was neatly stowed away, leaving me free to cope with the proper protocol of handshakes and curtsey.

Hermès bag

Gucci shoulder strap feedbag with the green and red webbing stripe. Stands up to any weather, holds a lot, perfect with sports clothes.

Gucci shoulder bag

Printed silk scarves from Hermès and Gucci are as close to works of art as fashion can get. With care they'll last for ever.

Gucci belt with gilt double Gs buckle. Can be attached to different coloured leather straps.

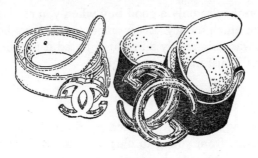

Gucci belts

Detractors of SS's claim that all women want a uniform, and maybe that's partly true; playing safe can make you feel sure, but I also see them as investments, and fashion dividends will come in year after year.

Imitations

Status symbols are usually copied, and it's perfectly all right to get the copy if it's a really good one, which means careful study of the original. The point is not only to have something well designed, but also to fool people.

I'm all in favour of buying imitations of high fashion, or as they say in the rag trade, 'knock offs', but it's better to go without rather than buy a weak alternative. If something is not right in the first place it never will be. To buy copies you have to recognize a classic: which copies are fabulous, which are fraudulent, and who's selling which version.

Start by being aware what name designers are doing each season. Then when looks are interpreted less expensively, you can zero in on what's right for you.

If something looks cheap but is expensive, it's useless, but if something costs very little, but looks like a million pounds, it's terrific. I hate anything that looks common, but I adore a bargain that looks like a luxury.

There does come the day when the imitations start costing nearly as much as the original, so then buy the original. Copies, unhappily, are never quite the same, either in quality or workmanship, so they're only a good buy when you're getting a lot of style for not much money. Every single time I have bought something that was only nearly all right, I hated it and never wore it. Second best is just not good enough.

Age

It's astonishing how many women go through life making only one transition: from young to old; but life just isn't that simple. All of us turn thirty one day and that means re-thinking what we look like. We're not as fresh as we were at eighteen, but on the other hand all my friends look better now than they did at twenty; except for Maggie, and at school she used to be the most striking one of all. But she hated getting older, refused to admit she was, and now, dressed in second-hand tat, wearing transparent dresses, she looks sad and a little dreary.

The rest of us have all got rid of the last vestiges of puppy fat and teenage acne; we've come to terms with our looks, and know more now about how to make the best of them.

It's not just birthdays that should make us sit up and reassess ourselves, but what stage our life has reached. As students we could live in jeans and jumpers; then comes job hunting time and going to an office every day where appearance counts as a part of job performance. Smart clothes do help you make your way up the ladder.

Marriage may change your life by taking you out of the rat race so that you revert to casual clothes for day, and only need good things for dinner parties and entertaining, or you may keep working and dress in the same style, but in a more sophisticated manner.

Children come, you're tied down looking after them, and the practicality of being able to throw everything in the washing machine comes first and foremost in your mind.

The day dawns when the children are all at school, and suddenly your life opens up again; you're older, your figure has changed, not necessarily for the better, and you look like a weak imitation of the pretty girl you were ten years ago.

Now is the time to change your look, first because it will give you a new surge of self-confidence, secondly because if you're going to enter the job market again you must look right. The polish that age brings should be reflected in your appearance.

Turning thirty was my most momentous birthday: not just because it was an age I'd always wanted to be: out of the terrible teens, away from the tense twenties; it was the start of a decade in which to flower. I think a woman's body and face flourish in her thirties, but then the forties loom.

Many women in their early forties have been married nearly a quarter of a century; and there's often a twenty-year-old daughter who's bright and sparkling with all the goodies ahead. If she's stayed at home raising the children, maybe she wants to work now; if she had a career, maybe it's time to get out of the rat race. The lines by her eyes and at the side of her mouth turn down, and the breasts and bottom are beginning to sag. Psychologically and physically, the fortieth birthday has to be a time of stern reassessment.

The most important thing is to be yourself; not start a wild search for your lost youth. Always remember that the swiftest way to grow stale is to stand still. Clothes that are too young paradoxically make their wearer look older. Over thirty, it's smarter to avoid the zany and kinky department. It's time to work a bit harder, get more organized, exhibit a bit of sophisticated glamour. The most ageless clothes I know of are those well-cut classic styles that appear to work together by chance, but in fact are carefully edited and always look marvellous. It's an air of throwaway chic that comes with experience.

3 ❧ Clothes

Fashion

Coco Chanel used to say that fashion worked when it caused you to notice the woman; it failed when you noticed what she was wearing.

The prime requisite for becoming a fashion authority is to have a completely open mind, ignoring the vulgarity of anything new. It exists to be adapted to you, not the other way around. Clothes do make the man, and they allow you to live out your visual fantasies, while pleasing others in the process.

It is absurd to put fashion on a pedestal and elevate it to the level of an art form. Clothes are only body coverings which reflect our personalities and are a means of expression. Fashion has to be fun, it has to make you feel good, and it has to add a spark to your life. If it doesn't, then it's not working for you. There may be a time when fashion is exactly suited to your face and figure; the rest of the time you have to find what can be adapted to you.

Today we have the exciting, exhilarating freedom to wear anything that suits us, but it often takes a little while to develop a strong personal fashion statement. Fashion normally evolves fairly slowly; too many radical changes terrify women to the point when they quietly retreat into their cupboards and stop buying, as witness the midi fiasco in 1970.

Choose the look that suits you. Look for trends, go with them and ignore the fads, which are not investments, just manufacturers' passing fancies. There is very little new in fashion. Things have been done other times, other ways, perhaps even for the other sex: pants for women, kilts for men. Before the Industrial Revolution, everything was made by hand and had to last a long time, so fashions changed slowly. Today everything is made by machine, so a rapid turnover is the norm.

Being in fashion today means clothes that are comfortable, functional and reflect your personality and taste. Feel pretty, feel sexy; don't wear stiff constructed garments and starched fabrics. Move as if your clothes were a second skin. Use clothes to emphasize your uniqueness, and never be a carbon copy of anyone, or any look. Let your clothes reflect different moods, different settings, different personalities. Fashion will change, but anything that is intrinsically well designed will remain in fashion for ever.

Clothes reflect the economic climate: when times are good, women bare their body; when times are bad they cover up for self-protection. The booming sixties fostered the mini; but in the seventies' recession, skirts fell as rapidly as the stock market. In boom times, it's fashionable for women to be skinny; but when the going gets rough, the well-padded female form is considered beautiful, as if to show that her male protector can afford to keep her well fed.

The fast pace of today's world has killed women's involvement with fashion. That deep abiding lust for clothes flew out of the window, along with the little dressmaker and the long hours spent on co-designing and collusion at home. We no longer have the free hours when we brushed our hair, did our nails, experimented with the most effective place for a beauty spot.

James Laver, the famous fashion historian, gave this list in his book, *Taste and Fashion*:

INDECENT	10 years before its time
SHAMELESS	5 years before its time
OUTRÉ (DARING)	A year before its time
SMART	. . . .
DOWDY	A year after its time
HIDEOUS	10 years after its time
RIDICULOUS	20 years after its time
AMUSING	30 years after its time
QUAINT	50 years after its time
CHARMING	70 years after its time
ROMANTIC	100 years after its time
BEAUTIFUL	150 years after its time.

The Haute Couture

Sadly, times have changed, and it looks unlikely that I'll ever have a couture dress made to order; though my predecessor at the *Sunday Times* always ordered dresses when she was in Paris for the twice-yearly showings. I first went to Paris and Rome for the shows in 1973, and with gratitude inherited Ernestine Carter's spindly gold chair, front row centre. I'd often heard the story of the fashion editor who, in 1947, completely missed the point of Christian Dior's 'New Look', because she was seated so far back that she couldn't see he had dropped the hem line from the wartime austerity of knee length to twenty-five yards of swirling fabric just above the ankle.

We may never own a couture original, or less expensive line-for-line copies; but the High Street stores are affected by the great couturiers, so it filters down to all of us eventually.

The truly talented designers work in an evolutionary manner: one season's designs leading logically to the next. There are rarely such revolutionary changes that, suddenly, everything looks dated. It was often said that the great thing about a Balenciaga collection was its familiarity. He contended that women didn't change every season, so why should their clothes? Fabric changed, colours varied, details altered, but the basic shape remained the same.

The real power of Paris lies in starting trends, and it's only in the last decade that fashion stopped filtering down from the elegant top end of the market to the masses. In 1968 the student riots erupted all over Paris, and Yves St Laurent showed a khaki collection of fatigue clothes that didn't look a million miles away from army and navy surplus.

Despite the astronomical price for a couture dress, the big houses don't make money on clothes; they make their millions on their scents. Chanel may be the best known couturière in the world, but it's more for her No 5, than for her sleek little suits.

It takes more endurance than intelligence to report on the collections. Indeed, my most overwhelming impression was how uniformly ugly fashion editors' knees are! In Rome, the best performance at each of the four or five shows a day was American-born, Italian-married Countess Consuelo Crespi who works for

Vogue, and who would sweep in to take her front row seat attired in an outfit from that particular designer's last collection, which seemed a flattering, if expensive, compliment. I liked her style.

Basic Wardrobe

Don't just buy, compose. Anyone really well dressed organizes her wardrobe as a whole. The less money you have, the more imperative it is to get your priorities right and buy clothes according to a carefully considered plan.

Look at it like a grocery list: anything you can't do without is protein. The extras, the things that will add pazazz and razzle-dazzle are the carbohydrates. These you buy as you can afford to. Man can live on meat and two veg alone, but he'll die of malnutrition on potato crisps.

When you shop, AMORTIZE. The more often you're going to wear something, the more you pay. If you wear something daily, it costs minute fractions of pennies per wear; that's amortizing. It's the dress that stays in your cupboard that's the most expensive one in your wardrobe.

Except for long evening dresses, and really rough heavy clothes for country excursions, everything I wear can go from morning through dinner when necessary. My wardrobe revolves around skirts, some of them plain wools, some printed, and a few in luxurious night-time fabrics. With them go a myriad of shirts, waistcoats and pullovers, pulled together by an assortment of belts.

The more simple your clothes, the more stylish you're going to look, and the shrewd woman mixes several price levels together. Pull your clothes together, don't just pull them on.

It took me a long time to realize how few clothes most elegant women have. I once trotted off to the Ritz to have tea with Gloria Guinness, the incomparable Mexican beauty who is married to a handsome and charming financier. She had transformed the faded pink glory of her suite with myriad luxuries that made the room as personal as any in her own home and, in the midst of it, she perched, in black shirt, black skirt, and black cardigan draped over her shoulders. In the course of conversation she gave me three pieces of advice which I've followed ever since.

First, 'If you can only afford to wear one colour, make it black, and no one will know whether it's couture or chain store.' I must add that she was wearing her simple shirt and skirt as a backdrop for the most luminous rope of pearls I've ever been close to; but I took her advice anyway.

Second, 'Always put your money into shoes and handbags. Leather never lies, and it has to be good. People look first at your face, then at your feet.'

Third, 'Buy clothes you love, and wear them over and over again. Overwhelm with the simplicity of your appearance. Black goes anywhere, any time. For the day, a black skirt and shirt; at night a simple black dress should form the basis of any wardrobe.'

Choose clothes that are so timeless you'll still be pleased with them years from now, and classics are clothes that last, are dateless and don't disappoint. An investment is something that continues to give you pleasure long after the novelty is over. The best things in life may not be free, but they do last.

When I was twenty I thought I was the bee's knees. I was earning about £20 a week and God knows how I bought the clothes I did. I had dresses for the office; dresses to go on a date; clothes for country weekends; specialized sportswear; cocktail dresses; and long evening gowns. I dressed exactly like my mother, only I was twenty-five years younger.

Today, the clothes I buy are interchangeable and, with bits and pieces added or subtracted, they can be worn anywhere and any time. There is nothing more depressing than a cupboard of barely worn, slightly passé, clothes. If you're bored with something that's well worn, you won't have a guilty conscience at giving it away.

One thing about growing up is that you no longer grow out of things. Over the last fifteen years I may have given clothes away because I hated them; or because after the death of the mini they were too short; but I don't remember throwing anything away because it was literally worn out. If you work to keep your weight level, and your body in good shape, your clothes should last you indefinitely.

Shopping

Men's second favourite fantasy is that any woman, given the choice, would spend all day shopping. How wrong they are! I loathe shopping and so does every woman I know. The crowds, the discomfort, the disappointment and so rarely the joy of finding exactly what one wants, at a price one can afford.

I now have a perfect system. I do only two shopping forays a year. I look at all the latest fashion magazines, which start pin-pointing looks, colouring and accessories in their pre-spring and autumn issues; and I reassess what's already in my cupboard to see what could be revived if something were added.

I'm lucky to live in London, but if you have to make a major excursion to buy clothes, clip out pictures of everything you like in magazines. You will often find the same look to them, many may be by the same designer, and if you are lucky, many will be in stock at just one or two of the major stores. Pin all your finds on a bulletin board, and you'll probably discover what very strong taste you have.

In shopping, getting what you want with the least amount of desperation is like planning a military campaign. Even if I'm so broke that I can only afford to buy from the cheapest chain stores, I'll first spend an hour combing through an expensive store to see what the clothes look like. Looking at well-made high fashion clothes, helps you identify the real, moderately priced bargains.

Comparison shopping is important because it gives you a realistic idea of what current costs are, and when you've looked at enough cheapies, you may well decide to sink all your money into one good thing because it's so well made. At least I hope you will. In the long term, invest in quality.

Window shopping is also invaluable; I adore walking anyway, and I plot my route to pass as many stores as possible. It's worth putting up with the aggravation of jostling crowds to make one's way down the main shopping street to see the brilliant merchandising displays that festoon the windows. Take buses or walk so that you can see as much as possible. I often get inspiration and discover another way to wear something from a well-dressed mannequin.

Take a look at new shops, so that you won't get into a fashion rut, and never be afraid of saleswomen. For years, people have complained to me that they're terrified to go into a place like Gucci, which is one of my favourite shops, because the sales people are such dragons. But if someone says to me, 'Can I help you?', I take that as meaning 'help', not 'buy or get out'. My automatic answer is always, 'just looking, thank you', and then if I do find something I like, I'll go back and ask for assistance. Never let anyone intimidate or pressure you, they're there to serve you.

If you're on a tight budget, get to know a few shops well, and make friends with one of the saleswomen. It's easier for them to sell you something if they know your taste, and they're more willing to go to extra trouble getting something special for you if you're a regular.

If there's something you desperately want, but really can't afford, ask them to let you know if it goes in the sale. Try going in the afternoon of the day before a sale begins. They're usually beginning to put out the merchandise, and often you get a preview, either buying then and there, or else getting it put away until the next morning.

When I started doing my radio programme, I'd have a list of stores to go round, usually escorted by their PR lady, who was obviously anxious for me to find lots of things I liked; but in fact, shopping is usually a matter of finding just one or two things, and it's a question of leg work till you know where to look.

1 Keep in mind unlikely places. If you're small you'll save a packet by buying plain button-down coloured shirts, bikinis, kilts, pullovers, jeans, sportswear in the children's and teens departments. The quality is as good, but prices are much lower. Because of the proportions, separates will probably fit better than any one-piece garment.

2 For outdoor gear, boys' and men's departments often have great buys: jeans, shirts, sweaters, scarves, hunting and fishing bags, tee shirts, and bush jackets.

3 There are only two seasons, summer and winter, and summer clothes worn in layers can, if necessary, take you through the coldest weather. The most elegant wardrobe in the world can be built around skirts, a pair of trousers, a

jacket, a raincoat, an assortment of shirts and pullovers, and one dressy dress or shirt.

4 Never shop without a clear idea of what you need.

5 Never buy when you're in a mad rush.

6 Never shop for a special occasion at the last minute, when you have to have something even if it turns out to be a mistake.

7 Never go shopping when you're depressed, or later you'll be just as depressed by what you bought.

8 Don't buy anything you're not sure you can use.

9 Never shop accompanied by children. They'll distract you, rush you, and you'll compromise in order to get done in a hurry.

10 Don't go shopping with a friend. Emotion, jealousy, one-upmanship all start playing a part.

11 Make up your face, fix your hair, look elegant, it will not only make you feel more self-confident, it will get you better service if you look as if you've got taste and money.

12 If you know that what you'll be trying on needs boots, wear them. If you're searching for an evening dress, take along any special shoes you'll want to wear. Something as basic as heel height makes a big difference to how clothes look.

13 Once you've trained yourself to think of everything in terms of what it goes with, you'll find that such thinking becomes automatic.

14 Jumble Sales, usually held to aid a good cause, mushroomed overnight when inflation reached double figures. Only you can decide if you're willing to wear other people's clothes; I'm not, but that's me. Two rules only: Get there early, the good things go first; clean or wash everything you buy.

A real bargain always looks as if it cost more than it did. Austerity chic means spending money where it shows, and skimping where it doesn't. We're straight back to status symbols again: all you need is one classy thing to upgrade everything else. If you had unlimited money, you could afford to buy a different drop dead outfit for every big occasion; but if, barring a big Pools win, you'll always have more taste than cash, you've got to stick to the basics. Dress down, eliminate the junk, and lovingly care for your body and your clothes. That's style.

Sales

A bargain isn't a bargain isn't a bargain if you end up never being able to wear it. Something bought on the spur of the moment that turns out to be a mistake is an expensive luxury.

Field's Rule is:
1 Never buy anything because it might be useful in the future. It has to be wearable today, right now, or don't get it.
2 If you'll need new accessories for your purchase, or something major like a coat or jacket to go with it, forget it.
3 Stock up twice a year in the sales on bras, knickers, tights, stockings, gloves and scarves.
4 A bargain is an extravagance if it needs a major alteration.
5 Sales are for investment buys such as coats, long dinner dresses, handbags, luggage, shoes and boots. In all these areas you can plan ahead. Who says you have to have your heavy coat ready to wear on 1 October? It doesn't really get cold enough to wear until December, so sit tight for three more weeks. With luck the temperature will soar, and you'll find a coat at half price on 27 December.
6 Don't waste time buying tat at half price. It should only have cost half the price in the first place.

Sales are planned with only one object in mind – to seduce us. They've got nothing to do with poverty or wealth. You should see the queues of millionaires milling around in the cold the first day of Burberry's winter sale.

Fit and Proportion

If you train your eye to only one thing, please let that be a sense of proportion; the symmetry that balances skirt length to heel height; shoulders to hip width; collar line to sleeve; hair shape to length of face and neck. It has all to do with scale; your body and the balance of what you want to add.

If you're big, you need bold shapes that balance your size; if you're tiny, you want to be sure you're not overwhelmed. This doesn't mean no prints, no stripes, no capes, no anything, whatever your size: it just means choose one that's in proportion to the rest of you.

It may take your eye some time to accept a new shape. Then, maybe months later, you'll suddenly wonder why you didn't see it all the time. In the early sixties, Courrèges had an enormous influence on fashion with his short dresses carefully balanced by white, knee-high, low-heeled boots. When done right, it looked fabulous from head to toe, but when done wrong – stiletto heels, bouffant hair, and mid-calf length, it was a disaster.

Vidal Sassoon's geometric haircut was the solution to the new proportions in dress. The Roger Vivier low-heeled, buckled shoe balanced the mini skirt. Ten years ago we wore galoshes when it poured; now we collect boots because their proportion is needed to balance long full skirts.

We all have special figure problems, and we all eventually learn tricks of camouflage. I find that what works best for me is to wear things that are either narrow on the top and fuller on the hips, or vice versa. Remember that the wrong shape is even worse than the wrong colour. One destroys your looks completely, the other only diminishes them.

Don't expect any dress bought off the rack to fit perfectly. It invariably needs some alteration, so pin and pull till the shoulders are in the right place, the waist sits right, and the hem is even all around. It's nearly impossible now to find a little lady who sews and doesn't charge the earth, but clothes still need to be properly fitted. A size 10 dress from a chain store is designed to fit a huge number of people, and none of those ladies will have exactly the same measurements and proportions as you.

1 Don't wear anything until it fits perfectly.
2 Never get talked into a wrong, unalterable size. But consider one size smaller than you need and having it let out in only one spot, if the alternative is a large alteration to take it in all over. Be sure inside seams are generous enough for this.
3 Aside from how sloppy they look, clothes that don't fit

well get out of shape much more quickly. Any style that is closely fitted gets distorted by the body within. If the fit is wrong, then the wear and tear is uneven.

4   Once your clothes fit perfectly, you can stop worrying about how you look, and concentrate on what you are doing.

5   Check that the hem is perfectly even.

6   Are the shoulders tight and high enough? Especially now that my hair is short, I find that a shoulder just an inch too wide makes any garment look wrong, as well as being uncomfortable. I also like the very high, small, Coco Chanel armhole.

7   Remove belt tabs, and replace any self-fabric belt on an inexpensive dress with a good leather one.

8   Small decorative bows should be removed, and replace cheap buttons with good ones.

Check the overall proportion of your outfit in a full-length mirror every time you dress to go out. Look at your face, then your hair, and finally the overall impression. Proportion is all the lengths of your body: your skirt length, sleeve length, jacket and bodice lengths, and finally your hair-do.

Colour

Colour co-ordination is the magic key to dressing well on a strict budget. Since your money is limited, every single item in your wardrobe must go with everything else. Impulse buys are out. Clothes in way-out colours spend most of the time in the cupboard. However, there are no firm don'ts any more about what colours go with which. No longer are there rules about always matching your shoes and handbags.

Twice a year, in autumn and spring, fashion designers herald two or three colours as the big ones for the coming season. Check the new combinations out, and see whether one new garment, or an accessory, in the latest colour, teamed with what you already have, can make old clothes new and fresh.

1   If a colour is currently fashionable but you loathe it, ignore it.

2 Light or bright colours attract; dark or neutral shades have the opposite effect.

3 Put an eye-catching colour next to your face so as to focus attention there.

To look long and lean, dress all in one colour. I feel uncomfortable wearing prints, as if my little face were lost in a vast muddle, so most of my clothes are solid colours, and any print I succumb to is usually on a small scale, and muted in colour.

For standing out in a large crowd, such as a wedding, always wear a pale, solid coloured outfit. With all the other ladies done up like Christmas trees, you look tranquil in the middle of all the fuss. Not original this, Princess Grace stole the spotlight at Princess Anne's wedding in her cream cape and white mink hat.

Never arbitrarily decide a colour is not for you and think that means for ever. As we get older, our skin and hair tones change, and colours that may not have suited us in the past now look well. I used to steer clear of beige, but now, with special attention to my make-up, it looks swell. Use the colours on your face to make the most of your clothes.

Fabric

Fabrics are seductive and sensual: the softness of velvet, cashmere and silk; the crunchiness of corduroys and tweed; the pull of knits; the slide of lush lingerie. I want my body to move against clothes and take pleasure in them – not that dreadful clammy non-porous feeling of synthetics.

The quickest give-away to cheap clothes are sleazy fabrics. In addition to their dreadful feel they usually come emblazoned with wild prints and garish colours.

There is no economy in cheating on fabric; cotton and wool look better, last longer, and are easier to look after. Choose a plain cotton shirt any day over a cheap rayon. And although we've been told for years that crease-resistant fabrics are going to revolutionize our life styles, I've yet to own anything that doesn't wrinkle, either on me or when packed for travelling.

I've learnt my lesson about investing in silk shirts. Even though labels tell you they can be handwashed if you're gentle, I've found that they never look right again, and that ironing them is pure murder. So, buy silk if you can't resist, but count on dry cleaning expenses as a heavy part of the price.

Some people have an uncomfortable problem with static electricity; synthetic fabric slips climb up, or clothes crackle when taken on or off. Try putting a little fabric softener in the rinse when you wash them; like hair conditioner after a shampoo, it calms down the electricity.

Antique and Second-Hand Clothes

When I was growing up, wearing someone else's old clothes was a secret kept hidden from even your most intimate friends. I'm afraid I've still got the same feeling: that there's something musty and unclean about them.

Antique fashions now fetch extraordinarily high prices, and specialized shops dealing in them have sprung up everywhere. Auction galleries hold special sales, and old-clothes stalls can be found in every street market.

Dress Agencies, on the other hand, handle modern clothes, usually on consignment from their owners. To find a nearly new Bill Gibb or Jean Muir, you've got to wade through an unbelievable amount of junk, but if you can bear it, join the scrum.

Army–Navy Surplus

This became high-price fashion when Yves St Laurent picked it up from the French student revolutionaries in 1968. It's a definite look; I don't think it suits most of us, but it's fine for the outdoor life, and the prices are rock bottom.

Bathrobes and Negligées

Have two. One terry cloth, which year round you can slip into after the bath, cosy and practical. It can be slung into the washing machine, but the threads get so badly pulled that it looks like a rag overnight. I wash mine by hand, and then stick it into the drier.

Have a second one which is pretty and feminine for over the breakfast table. If you travel a lot, choose a light fabric for easy packing.

Beachwear

There are two necessities. The first is a bathing suit to get wet in, and the second is something to dry off and cover up in.

Diana Vreeland once announced that the bikini was the most important invention since the Atomic Bomb. If she's right, it was with just about the same disastrous effect.

On any beach, 90 per cent of the women in a minuscule two-piece should be arrested; never was the word camouflage more relevant. Why are so many women willing to flaunt unattractive features? With a little judicious shopping, they could find a one-piece suit that reveals their best points, and hides the rest.

Since most bathing suits are made of synthetic fibres, all of which are affected by salt water, heat, chlorine and the chemicals in suntan lotion, I think it's ludicrous to spend £30 on something that will only last for a couple of months. All the big chain stores carry a smashing selection; both in styles and sizes. The bigger you are, the darker a colour you should choose, and look for either a solid colour or a small-scale print.

It's currently fashionable to have various bits and pieces of metal attached as decoration but, beware, they get scorchingly hot in the sun.

As a cover up, nothing is more practical than a cotton khanga, a printed 2 × 3-foot piece of fabric. You can buy them everywhere very inexpensively, or make one yourself from a pretty sheet. Tie it as a sarong at your hip; knotted at your bustline so it looks like a mini dress; or like a toga, wrapped around and over one shoulder.

An agonizing problem may arise if you are scarred after an operation or breast surgery. Do you hide away in the dark, or face the world? If you've had a mastectomy, there are specialists who make suits in which you can appear on any beach.

Clothes

The Khanga

like a toga wrapped around
and over one shoulder

tied like sarong at hip

knotted at bustline as mini-dress

Coats

Coats are all-impoⅰtant because that's what people see you in first. Whatever style you choose, make sure the shoulders fit perfectly, and that the length is long enough to go over everything.

If you can afford only one, start off with a classic beige trenchcoat: epaulets, big pockets, raglan sleeves; and don't do up the belt properly, but knot it like a bathrobe. Traditionally, they have a pleat in the back which is supposed to give you additional leg room when you're striding over the moors. Always keep the small fastening open. I don't know the reason why, but chic people always do.

The best, and most famous trenchcoat is a Burberry. Even if you can't afford it, try one on, and note how it fits before you look for a good copy; or give up lunches, cigarettes and the Pub, for the month of December, and spend the money saved in their winter sale. Men's stores have some very good coats which, in a small size, ought to fit you perfectly. When it's cold, wear it over a heavy sweater; in the summer it goes over a cotton sundress. Some even come with zip-in heavy linings.

Next on your list should be a big loose swagger coat: patch pockets, big buttons, and often a deep pleat down the back. On the coldest days, this one goes over lots of layers, and looks smashing in loden green, or a nubby tweed.

A black woollen cape goes over anything but, if you don't have one, use a shawl as an evening wrap. Nothing looks more tacky than a street coat over a long dress.

Steer clear of any vinyl rainwear. It makes you hot and sticky; and the rain slides straight down the coat and into your boots.

Culottes

A big look the last few years, and a safe alternative to either trousers or a skirt.

Dresses

For a while, as the great skirt length debate raged, dresses became much less important. Now there are masses of pretty ones around, ranging from the classic shirtwaist to the smock inspired by St Laurent.

Chanel launched the Little Black Dress in the 1920s, and made it a household word. Today my LBD is a skirt and shirt, but it's the thought that counts. The secret of it remains the same, something that looks good, any time, anywhere.

If you like wearing dresses, an alteration lady is a necessity. You can't fake it as easily as when you're wearing separates. A bad fit makes even a designer original look like a rag.

1 Check that the shoulders are cut nice and narrow; and that the collar doesn't stand away at the back of your neck.
2 Alter the bodice if necessary. If it's too big, it will make your bustline look matronly.
3 Check the hem to make sure it is perfectly even.
4 If there is a matching belt, it's probably going to be plastic and horrid. Switch it for a smashing leather one from your cupboard, and cut off the belt hooks that add a hick touch to any dress.
5 If you have an old dress that bores you to tears, but the fabric is fabulous and the skirt is a good shape, and there's a waistline seam; cut off the top, leaving plenty of fabric so that you can turn over a new waistband.

Ethnic Styles

In the beginning, they were cheap and cheerful; cheesecloth was seen everywhere, and as package airline travel became part of our lives, we all came home wearing souvenirs of our travels.

Today it has all become a little tatty, and I think the ethnic look has definitely had its day. It's no fun looking like everyone else, especially when that look has degenerated into a sloppy, unkempt mess.

Evening Dresses

There are two kinds of evening dresses. The first is for those once-in-a-lifetime occasions when price is no object, and your only criterion is to be the most attractive woman in the room. I've had to attend that sort of party as a journalist, and the women who catch everyone's attention are usually dressed in something devastatingly simple.

Two years ago Caroline Charles made me a wonderful tomato red, silk crêpe, strapless dress, which upstaged every ruffle and glittering diamond in the room. There are three colours that are always fabulously effective on drop dead occasions: black, red or white; never a print, as it doesn't stand out in the mob.

For dinner parties, either as a guest or a hostess, I find funny little dresses in all sorts of places. Usually on sale, most of them cost from £10 to £20, and they go on year after year. Look in beachwear departments for caftans, teenage departments for the milkmaid look, lingerie departments for At Home things.

Most of them are easily washed cotton, and I keep them for always. I may be bored with one this year but, two years from now, it will look fresh to my jaded eye, or I'll suddenly try it with a different jacket, shawl or belt: shirt underneath, or waistcoat over. Sometimes it's worth shortening to mid-calf and giving it a new lease of life that way.

Furs

Some women would do anything for diamonds, others would rather give their all for a fur coat. I'm easy: wearing fur is a wonderfully sensual experience, and nothing else in the world is quite as warm.

I found my first fur coat on sale for one hundred dollars. It was a cream coloured Belgian Lapin, which turned out to be rabbit with a French accent. That coat got me through six winters, and was one of the best investments I've ever made. The only thing wrong with rabbit, which is around in quantity, and no more expensive than a good woollen coat, is that it sheds, and you're always covered in hairs.

If you do love furs, and hate being cold, I think they are worth the money. They may be expensive but, with careful attention, they last indefinitely.

All good department stores have a salon with a trained furrier in charge. Discuss your likes and dislikes, what you want the coat for, and how often you intend to wear it. All this has a bearing on the type of fur you choose. Try on dozens of different colours and styles, so that you can narrow down the look you like. Your final choice may be something you'd never thought of.

1   If you have a cool dark cupboard, it's safe to store it there in the summer, under a cotton cover, but never plastic. If not, pay the approximate £5 it costs to keep it in a furrier's cold storage.

2   Never let a fur get near direct heat.

3   If your coat gets caught in the rain, hang it up in an open place and gently towel it down. Let it stay in a warm dry corner for a few hours, and then towel it again.

4   Set the top hairs in an upward direction, by stroking with a slightly damp, gentle clothes brush.

5   Fur is just like your hair: it gets greasy from contact with your skin. Get it cleaned in the autumn before you begin to wear it; and if it's looking dull after a lot of wear, again at the end of January.

Jackets

If you can afford only one jacket, make it a black velvet blazer which you'll be able to wear over everything you own. Make sure the shoulders are cut tight and narrow, and the sleeves are long enough. If the buttons are cheap, change them for good ones.

If you often wear trousers, or if your skirts are at least mid-calf length, and quite straight, the Hacking style shape is perfect. If your figure is more hour glass, and your skirts usually full, choose one of the newer hip-length ones with slightly shaped waist.

The most practical point about jackets is that in this era of changing hem lengths you don't have to worry that a major investment looks suddenly out of date. Make sure the proportions between your top and bottom halves are balanced.

Large Sizes

Sensible manufacturers are finally beginning to realize that large women are just as interested in being well dressed as small ones; but if you're bigger than a size 14, you will still have a very limited choice.

Luckily, fashion at the moment is full of loose-fitting, unconstructed dresses which may solve your problem. But in the long term, if you've got a big build, and losing weight is difficult, you should learn to sew. Even if you only learn to make up three or four patterns, you'll be able to use beautiful fabrics, and to make sure that the length and sleeves are long enough.

If your legs are large, always wear boots, or else dark stockings and plain dark shoes.

Leather

Coats, skirts and jackets in leather are not always excessively expensive, but they do need specialist cleaning, and that is extremely pricey. Suede shows every mark, and creases quite badly. Although it can be dyed to beautiful shades, it quickly shows any wear and tear, and make-up and natural skin oils will soon stain the neckline and cuffs. Pigskin stands up better to the elements, but it's not heavy enough to provide any real warmth.

Never attempt to clean or wax leather yourself, leave it to the experts.

Mail Order

If you live deep in the country, and making even the shortest trip for the basic necessities turns into a major excursion, Mail Order catalogues are probably the perfect solution to your fashion problems.

Mail Order houses all offer value for money; but they are not necessarily cheap, and you lose the advantage of comparison shopping in your local High Street.

Take advantage of Special Offers in magazines and newspapers. When I was at the *Sunday Times*, I started getting name designers to adapt one of their best-selling designs for us, and we had an enormous success with them. The prestige of the publication is behind what you order, and you can get a reasonable discount on what the same garment would cost in a shop.

Lady Antonia Fraser claims that she buys at least half her clothes this way.

Maternity

If you're lucky, you may find that until the very last months you're able to get away with fashionable clothes that are cut big and baggy in the first place.

1 Choose monocromatic colour schemes so that all of you looks longer and leaner.
2 Divert all the attention to your face with well-done make-up, clean shining hair, pretty earrings, a stylish scarf or an interesting necklace.
3 Wear low-heeled shoes and boots so that you don't walk awkwardly, and try to keep your posture as straight as possible. It won't merely make you look better, it will lessen the strain on your lower back.

Hospitals

Don't let anyone tell you that vanity is misplaced when you're ill. The first thing to do is to get out of those rough, open, uncomfortable hospital gowns, and into a nightgown of your own. Choose a washable material; one that's not transparent; and it's helpful to have something that unbuttons completely. Take along a sufficient quantity for you to have a clean one every day. Being ill is often very messy.

I use my boyfriend's shirts which are long enough to reach to my knees. Old and sloppy as they are, the material is as soft as silk, and the cheerful colours counteract the dreariness of being ill.

Have a wrap-around robe that is easy to get in and out of, and a pair of flat slippers or thonged sandals.

Leave any valuable jewellery at home; all you need is a watch. Bring along whatever day make-up you usually wear, scent, shampoo and some small face towels. However ill you feel, fixing your face will at least improve your morale. Have a selection of barrettes and hairbands to keep your hair looking neat and pretty. You may be too weak to get it washed as soon as it needs it.

Nightgowns and Sleepwear

What you wear in bed often varies according to circumstances; and wearing nothing is a great economy. Even if you don't wear a nightgown at home, you'll need one for staying with friends, or in a hotel. Look for an easy-care fabric, and if it's a full-length one, make sure it's wide enough for you to move around comfortably in your sleep. If you only wear them for decency's sake, choose black, and have done with it.

I can't imagine anything more uncomfortable than pyjamas, so I'll stay out of this one.

Separates

The multiplication table in any cupboard. Fifty pounds spent on separates goes a lot further than the same sum spent on one dress.

Shirts

I never throw a shirt away. In 1961, I wore a white shirt with a ruffled front for my school yearbook picture; and I still wear that shirt today, even if it's only five times a year.

Put together a shirt collection that includes nearly every colour in the spectrum, and have half a dozen styles, and assorted sleeve lengths to choose from. Ninety per cent of mine were good buys in some sale, and some of the older ones show up as collar and cuff trim under plain pullovers.

Cotton is the most practical, because it's easy to wash and iron. Real silk is extravagant, not because of the purchase price, but because it must be dry cleaned (see section on Fabric).

There is a new synthetic satin on the market which looks like a million pounds. Best of all, it irons like a dream.

1   For plain coloured cotton shirts, check out the boys' department, where they're cheaper.
2   Look in the men's department for big floppy shirts to be worn loose with a wide cinched belt; or tucked in over a polo neck.

3 To get the new 'Granpa' look from old shirts, carefully remove the collar from the collar band by slitting the stitches with a seam ripper. Then stitch the collar band back together again.

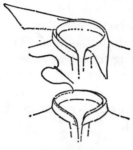

'Granpa' shirt

Shorts

If your legs are good, why not? But never on a city street. Floppy big ones make good thighs look even skinnier. Cutting off old jeans are a cheap alternative, and you can make them any length you like.

Skirts

It's perfectly feasible to have a wardrobe that will take you anywhere in the world, based on only three skirts. On the other hand, it's impossible to have too many, so just go on collecting them. I have been wearing Caroline Charles clothes since 1973, and some of my oldest skirts, in exceptionally pretty fabrics, are worn as often as my newest ones.

The Big Three:
1 A black skirt goes with everything. Choose the best quality fabric, wool or cotton, and as well made as you can afford. If it's straight, be sure it's lined so that it doesn't lose its shape. If it's full, a lining isn't necessary.
2 A floral print. If you can, find one that has a matching shirt so that you have a dress effect, but with the practicality

of two pieces. Choose a print that has several different shades in it so that you can wear it with various coloured tops.

3   The third can be tweed, solid or printed; it can be a tartan plaid, or striped; or if you love the blue jean look, find one made out of denim.

If you're going to wear boots every day, make sure the skirt length is long enough to cover the tops of them. The longer the length, the more expensive it's going to look anyway.

If you have any long skirts that you never wear, cut them to mid-calf length and give them a new lease of life.

Always put your skirt on over your head, or you may open up the hem with your foot.

Suits

The perfect solution to any tricky climate is a suit. It looks appropriate wherever you go, and whatever you do. At any hour, the all-in-one effect from a matching skirt and jacket has an elegant air, while you retain the convenience of separates. You will get so much wear out of a suit that it is worth spending more than you think you can afford. AMORTIZE.

There are two looks to go for: one is the casual sportif style in tweed, corduroy or pure wool. The jacket is a blazer cum hacking jacket, and the skirt a modified dirndl or pencil straight. Whichever material you choose, either piece can be worn on its own, putting together an almost unlimited number of different looks. Accentuate the country look of this with boots and a shoulder bag. When you're fitting the jacket, make sure the shoulders fit well, and that it doesn't pull too much when the buttons are done up.

The alternative is the classic Chanel suit, which has been going strong for the last forty years. There are usually half a dozen versions around; with an easily shaped A-line skirt, and a loose-fitting cardigan-style jacket, which has gilt buttons, silk braid trim and small decorative pockets. Often a chunky gilt chain is sewn into the hem of the jacket lining so that it hangs well.

The chic of the Chanel suit comes from high, tight armholes, narrow shoulders, and skinny sleeves, which are always long enough to hit the wrist bone. The blouse, often tying into a soft bow at the neck, is usually made from the same fabric as the jacket lining.

The true value of this suit is its timelessness. The classic length has always just covered the kneecap, and it has pretty well stayed there through mini and midi. Even the copies have a French panache about them that can't be ignored.

Sweaters

To be collected over a number of years. Each season brings with it new styles, but what is just as important is collecting a wide range of colours.

Start with lots of long-sleeved, skinny polo necks, which can go under other jumpers, a shirt, or on their own. A skirt and shirt are that much warmer, just by adding a jumper underneath.

Shetlands come in scrumptious colours, and are classic fashion in any part of the world. Build up a good wardrobe of the neutrals: black, white, beige, grey and navy.

Cardigans are a necessity, both for added warmth and as a fashion look. Have one solid one in a heavy cable stitch and a big sloppy shape. Another could be an adaptation of the beautiful designs by Missoni; cobweb fine knits in sophisticated patterns of stripes or herring-bone tweeds.

Never hang up jumpers, knitted dresses or knitted trousers. Keep them folded flat on a shelf, or they will stretch out of shape. I do hang up cardigans, as they take up so much room when folded.

Tee Shirts

A sizeable collection of tee shirts, accumulated over time, can form the basis of any warm weather wardrobe. A cotton skirt, and a pair of jeans, can find themselves transferred into a multiple of outfits based on different tops.

Tee shirts used to be round-necked, short-sleeved, and white. Then, suddenly, they began to be fashionable, and every summer finds at least four new shapes, and half a dozen new colours or prints. I think there's a connection between their rise in popularity and the bra-less look. If you don't have to worry about bra straps showing, or too revealing a silhouette, anything is possible.

Make sure your tee shirts are cotton for comfort, but otherwise find the cheapest you can.

Look after them carefully, and wash them by hand in cold water so that they don't lose their shape. I'm against dying them yourself as, in the heat, the colour may come off and stain your skin.

Buy an enormous one in the men's department, and wear it as a beach cover-up over your bathing suit.

Riding Clothes

If you ride a lot, you'll want proper breeches, hacking jacket and leather boots.

If you're just the occasional weekend rider, wear old stretched blue jeans; knee-high rubber Wellingtons which you can get in any children's shoe department and either a tweed jacket or waterproof anorak. Comfort is more important than beauty.

Ski Wear

The price of ski clothes has reached prohibitive heights in the last few years. It's not uncommon to find the latest French or Italian finery for as much as £175, but as more and more people take up the sport, the big chain stores are beginning to get on the band wagon.

Choose a solid colour, preferably dark, as you won't get so quickly bored as with a wild print or a neon bright shade. Don't let your gear be more impressive than your skiing.

Tennis Clothes

If you're one of those ladies who take their sports very seriously, and meet their friends three times a week to play, you've probably got a cupboard full of gear. If you only play occasionally at a club, or with smart friends, get a pair of plain white shorts, a short-sleeved cotton tee shirt and a vee-necked tennis sweater with a red/navy stripe around the neckline.

Plain white plimsolls and, if your legs aren't too good, bare legs

– so they'll look longer. If you're lucky enough to have skinny thighs, try the schoolgirlish look of white ribbed knee socks.

Ignore all those frilly little dresses, rick-rack trimmed skirts and ruffled knickers. Make sure your game is as good as your outfit.

If you play just once a year, and with very relaxed friends, wear blue jeans.

Trousers

If you have rotten legs and wear trousers as camouflage, or just hate wearing skirts, you probably collect trousers. If money is tight, wear jeans during the day, and invest in one impeccably cut pair of black woollen trousers that will look as well in the evening as they do during the day. Grey, navy or beige always look smart.

Trousers are the hardest thing to fit perfectly; you may have to try on a dozen different cuts before you discover the one that suits your measurements the best. Trousers that are long enough make your legs look longer. Be sure they at least skim the toe of your shoe.

If you rarely wear trousers, jeans are the answer. They're as old as the American gold rush, and as up to date as the latest style; but stick to the straight-leg look, and they won't be stamped any year in particular. Jeans are basic, and not to be messed around with.

Harriet took me to buy my first ever pair of jeans four years ago, and I couldn't believe that any rational person would be willing to constrict themselves into a denim corset but, after a couple of days, they had moulded to my body, and I began to understand not only their practicality, but also their sexual significance.

The only care jeans need is a machine wash, and then into the drier. After fifteen minutes or so, when they're just beginning to dry, take them out and pull the legs and waistband apart as hard as you can. This stops them from shrinking, which can be as much as 8 per cent. Jeans look good for years and, when they begin to stretch with age, wash and dry them into shape.

A good-looking variation is to tuck your oldest jeans into a pair of children's socks, so that they fit neatly into your knee-high boots. Another trick is to roll on a pair of brightly striped leg warmers, so that all that shows is a wide strip of denim thigh.

Underwear

The best thing about today's underwear is that there are so many styles, and so many price ranges, that you can switch around, not only to suit what you're wearing, but also to suit your mood.

1   Bras: Whatever shape your bust, and most of us are either grapefruits or bananas, the best bra to wear is the soft, gently shaped, 'no bra', that has tucks, and not darts. Wear flesh coloured ones under everything, and you won't need a colour assortment.

If you wear sundresses or sleeveless shirts in the summer, avoid the messy look of slipping straps, by sewing tiny lingerie straps in the shoulders. They're available in any haberdashery department. If you don't have any, use a safety pin as a temporary measure: attach it parallel to your shoulder bone, and let the strap slide through it.

Strapless dresses were much in vogue last summer. If you don't want to invest in a strapless bra; or go without; try either of these old model tricks. The first is band aids stuck right across your nipples. The other is a halfslip pulled up over your bust, and anchored by the elastic waistband.

2   Body Stocking: I can't imagine a single good reason why anyone would want to wear one, at any time.

3   Girdles: are the worst possible thing for the muscles in your stomach and bottom. Wear one long enough, and everything will turn to flab. Cheat by wearing a wide lace suspender belt and stockings. The belt should be tight enough over your pelvic area to hold in your stomach.

4   Knickers: come in three different styles. Minimal bikinis are so tiny that they make you feel young and sexy. Wear them over tights to help hold them up, and never wear them in such a loud print that it shows through your clothes. Don't wear bikinis under trousers, because the hip line elastic invariably shows, and it looks very tarty and messy. Either wear a pair of tights, or an old-fashioned pair of knickers which come up to the waistline.

Sexiest of all are the French-inspired, silky, lace-trimmed boxer shorts, which had a great revival a few years ago. In expensive satin fabrics from Janet Reger, they were pretty pricey, but now they've spread to chain store level. If you're the least big pudgy, this is the most flattering style, and they're very comfortable to wear. There are different colour combinations available, but the most authentic one is the so-called 'knicker pink'.

If you ever suffer from any sort of cystic disease, be sure to wear cotton knickers because it is both absorbent and porous.

5 Full Slips: unnecessary.

6 Ruffled Petticoats: are not only fashionable, they make any slightly too-short skirt instantly longer, and in the winter they add an additional layer of warmth. If you're economizing on your coat always substitute heavy stockings and a petticoat. It makes an astonishing difference to the warmth factor.

Even if you spend the minimum on lingerie, look for pretty feminine styles, in smooth silky fabrics. You'll know what's next to your skin; you'll move differently; you'll think about your body differently. Most important of all, make sure that no foundation ever shows through your clothes, it's not sexy; just plain tacky.

Wedding Attire

You will never spend as much time worrying about any dress as you do when choosing what to get married in.

If it is your first wedding you will probably choose a white dress, even if it's cotton instead of brocade, and looks more like an informal summer evening dress than the high-necked, long-sleeved model traditionally handed down from mother to daughter.

Forget anything practical like 'will it dye, and can I wear it again later?' I've never seen a dyed wedding dress that didn't look like a dyed wedding dress.

Decide the maximum you can afford to spend and stick to it. Buy plain white silk shoes at a chain store.

Keep the headdress simple, and if possible, borrow your veil from family or a friend.

Simple pearl button earrings are the only jewellery you need.

Bridesmaids' Dresses

Since bridesmaids usually have to pay for their own dresses, I think the bride should try and find as inexpensive ones as possible. The stores are full of pretty, reasonably priced evening dresses in a wide range of colours and prints; many of which are covered up enough to be proper for a religious ceremony. Also take a look in the lingerie department, as many At Home dresses are stocked there.

For a simple headdress, choose a plain, inexpensive straw hat and trim it with matching ribbon and a silk flower from any haberdashery department.

Work Clothes

There are two sorts: the first is that pair of old jeans and those worn-out shirts that I keep to wear when I'm painting the flat, polishing the floors or weeding the garden. All I want then are things I don't have to worry about, and something I can chuck into the washing machine.

But authentic work clothes have also become a fashion cult. Painters' overalls; boiler suits; white cotton waiters' jackets; and green surgical smocks have all been taken up by the trendies, until they became as expensive as a sensible outfit. To me, they're an affected extravagance. Better to spend your money elsewhere.

4 ❧ Accessories

Accessories

Accessories are the extras that add pazazz to everything you wear. Covet them; collect them; and learn to manipulate them, so that switching them around multiplies everything you own.

Start with the premise that anything that isn't an actual body covering is an accessory. Mine range in price from pennies (a big black silk rose that has appeared on at least eight different dresses) to £120 for my Gucci leather boots.

Accessories are serious when they're leather, because leather has got to be good or everything you're wearing looks tacky; and they're a giggle when they're the latest fad, like a punk rock safety pin brooch. Look for them in teenage boutiques, men's wear shops and tourist traps.

The clever use of accessories can completely change your look. Last year you'd wear your Granny smock loose with three little pouches strung around your neck on leather thongs, knee-high boots and big gypsy earrings. Now belt the waist with a narrow sash, drape a shawl around your shoulders, put high-heeled ankle-strap sandals on your feet and tuck a straw pouchette under your arm.

Never throw accessories out. Sometimes you may not wear something for a year or two, but sooner or later everything comes back into style. Two years ago, I bought a cream cotton Bill Gibb outfit, topstitched in red, to wear to Buckingham Palace for a drinks party Prince Philip was giving in honour of Bing Crosby. I already had beige shoes, so that was easy, but I still needed a handbag. There on the shelf was a flat red leather pouchette

57

which I had bought to wear with a light blue spring coat when I was thirteen. Out it came, and I've worn it steadily the last two summers.

On my last trip to New York, I extravagantly treated myself to an Yves St Laurent black velvet dinner suit. Back to the cupboard, and out came the black velvet envelope with tiny gold corners that my mother chose for my first grown-up dance, 50 per cent of my life ago.

Now you see why giving accessories storage space is always an economy in the end. They are the finishing touch, and this is where a collection of status symbols comes in handy. Keep an eye on the sales, and pick up special bits and pieces.

Belts

Can do more to change the proportions of an outfit than anything else. Whatever they cost, they're investment buying, and not to be tossed out at the end of the season. Collect interesting kinds of buckles, and wear them with different coloured leather belt bands.

I keep all mine rolled up on a shelf, and separated by colour. Gradually, I've accumulated different widths in all the basic shades like black, brown, red, beige and navy. At the end of the line are more unusual shades like olive green and deep purple.

High fashion this year are expensive twisted-cord belts. Create your own version by getting a yard of upholstery cord in a silky jewel colour, for a tenth of the price.

To avoid stretching a good leather belt in hot weather, hook a long skinny scarf through the belt loops of your jeans.

Boots

In the last five years, boots have become the most important accessory of all. I used to think they were to keep your feet dry in rotten weather but, at today's prices, I've changed my mind.

1 Have a pair of low-heeled rubber Wellingtons for days that really are wet, cold and dreadful. Choose black, wear them everywhere.

2 Leather boots are investments that are going to get a lot

of wear and tear, so get the best ones you can afford. Two years ago I got brown ones; this year I got black. I polish them every time I wear them; I get them re-heeled as soon as they need it; and for what they cost, they're going to have to last me a very long time.

Choose a classic, ungimmicky style; it won't date as quickly. Check to see if the soles are waterproof. If not, your local shoe-maker can add rubber soles. Get ones with a zipper; you'll do yourself an injury pulling them off otherwise. Make sure they're comfortable; boots are meant for walking.

To keep boots dust-proof while storing or for packing: use old pillow cases and tie them closed with a pretty ribbon.

Gloves

In the good old days, a lady wasn't a lady if she wasn't wearing white kid gloves. Now even the Queen wears suede fabric ones which can be easily washed; and the Duchess of Kent attends glamorous film premières in Zandra Rhodes' frills, and white cotton gloves up to her elbows.

I have a pair of short white kid gloves that I save to clutch for Royal Ascot or at a wedding. Otherwise, I only wear gloves in the winter when my nails get brittle, and cold hands make all the rest of me twice as chill. In the country, it's warm woollen mittens; in London, black leather gloves. I never throw out old odd gloves (I lose a lot), but save them to wear for weeding.

Wool-lined leather gloves really do keep you warm. If you live in a very cold climate, it's worthwhile investing in a pair, but they are much more bulky, very expensive, and I don't think they're a necessity for a moderate London winter.

Too short jacket sleeves can be easily camouflaged by wearing long gloves. Always make sure no skin shows between the glove and coat sleeve, it only makes a garment look skimpy.

Handbags

One superb quality bag that goes with you everywhere is better than half a dozen tatty jobs that will fall apart before you nod, and usually in front of a curious audience.

I buy one new handbag a year, usually on sale; and I've never yet thrown one away because it's worn out. I've given a couple away; Lucinda inherited a navy blue one I'd had since *Glamour* days, and she'll probably keep it going as long again.

During hot and sticky summer days, I carry a straw mesh envelope I found for £1 and use it as a pouchette. Not bad, and it's the same one the Editor of *Vogue* carries.

The only thing that does change about handbags is their shape, and the reasons behind a new look are often as social as they are design-inspired. In the 1920s coats were unfastened, and bodies slumped forward in order to keep them closed. Handbags came off their long gilt chains, and evolved into envelopes, dubbed pouchettes, that could be tucked under the arm. In the safe and satisfied swinging sixties, shapes were neat and tidy; and status consisted not just in sporting the Hermès H bag, or the Chanel quilted kidskin with chain handles, but in learning the graceful wrist grip, which showed up in photographs around the world when Jackie Kennedy became First Lady.

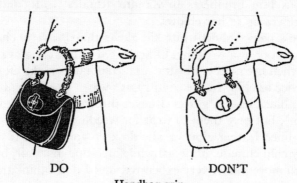

DO   DON'T

Handbag grip

Hold handbag so that handle is straight on in front of you. Slide arm around through the right-hand corner until hand extends past the left-hand side, now hold your arm into your side, and handbag is poised out of the way, and never over the stomach. A big help when you're constantly confronted by photographers.

In the seventies, Women's Lib began to take hold, and overnight everyone seemed to be lugging small suitcases around. They rapidly represented mobile offices: stuffed with address books, diary, files, calculator, chequebook, wallet, bills and perhaps a love letter or two.

Then the move for emancipation began to slow down, and we all found ourselves clutching neat little pouchettes again. I like carrying a small envelope with all the essentials, and a big canvas tote bag that slings over my shoulder, and holds not only all my working paraphernalia but a folding umbrella, book for the bus, and the groceries and laundry as well when necessary. Going into a restaurant, or meeting, I check the tote, and still have the pouchette at hand. This is the most practical alternative I've found to a briefcase, which I think looks clumsy, and oddly pretentious.

Last year the big tote bag fad was in gold or silver; and the look spread like wildfire. This year the school satchel look is big. Don't spend a lot of money on a tote bag; they're meant for wear and tear, and an expensive one won't look much better than a cheap one after a couple of weeks.

Try this test to see exactly how big a handbag you need. Weed out all the junk you normally carry. I bet 70 per cent of it sits in the bottom, and never sees the light of day. Treat yourself to a tiny leather diary and miniature address book. Have a neat leather wallet. Now pack them away in your usual bag. Use only the base where things rest. At the end of three days, does it still look half empty? Well then, you can do with a handbag half the size.

Keep your handbag just as clean as the rest of you. The sight of a tatty, messy interior is as repugnant as dirty underwear. Used tissues, old make-up, cancelled receipts and old bus tickets just won't do, not for me, not for you.

1 If you're going to have only one bag, make it black. Eventually add brown, beige, maroon or navy, if those are colours that work with lots of your clothes.
2 At night, carry a simple black cloth envelope. No trim, no glitter, and found in any High Street store.
3 Don't buy beaded bags, but see if you can unearth any antique ones from elderly relatives. I have two miniature beaded pouches, and one gold kidskin envelope that my grandmother bought in Paris in the 1920s, and I love wearing them.

4 For big canvas satchels with lots of straps and compartments, check stationers' and the children's department of any big store.
5 Take good care of your leather bags, but never use coloured polish on them. It will rub off on your hands and clothes. Use a neutral coloured wax, and buff to a high gloss.
6 For the country look, find a sporting goods shop where shooting bags and fishing baskets are a reasonable price.
7 Collect small metal boxes in the shape of animals, that can be found in market stalls and ethnic bazaars. Take one with you in place of an evening bag. Cartier calls them minaudières, and sells them for hundreds of pounds.

Handkerchiefs

Buy Kleenex.

Hats

Wearing a hat makes me feel sophisticated, scintillating and alluring. They're the icing on the cake, not a necessity; but if you like them, and I mean a proper, brimmed shape, not a knitted cap, start with one plain straw one that you can decorate with lots of different patterned ribbons. In the winter get a black felt one, and do the same thing. However, life's so relaxed these days, you can get away without ever wearing a hat, even at weddings if you like.

In 1971 I bought an inexpensive natural straw sombrero in New York and kept it on my head all the way from Manhattan to Nice Airport. I swept off the plane to find Mr Right waiting at the foot of the ramp; his plane had just got in from London, and we both thought I looked very soignée, so the hat was a great success. In seven years, that hat has taken me to five Royal Ascots and three weddings, and it has camouflaged countless hopeless hairdos. It has been decorated with skinny ribbons, wide sashes and various stick pins. I know it's always the same hat, but no one else does.

1 If you're looking for a hat to go with a specific outfit, take the garment shopping with you. The right hat has as much to do with proportion as it has with the shape of your face, so check how it looks both standing up and sitting down. Also check the dimensions from either side as well as straight on.

2   Any hat, whatever the shape, is going to flatten your hair. Hats also make your head perspire, which leaves your hair looking matted.

Hosiery

Considering how boring stockings are, it's ludicrous how important they are to the total look. Stocking colours are instant plastic surgery through optical illusion. Heavy legs look thinner in dark shades and matching shoes. Skinny stalks get the illusion of shape from the lighter shades.

I think brightly coloured tights should be left to the kids. Either wear black or pale natural shades.

If your legs are short, wear pale beige shoes with pale legs, or black shoes with black stockings, and you'll be surprised at how much longer your legs will look, and an added bonus is that your feet look smaller.

Mesh stockings can be very uncomfortable. The open construction allows the soles to rub against the inside of shoes, and I came away with some bloody blisters. Never again.

Patterned stockings are warmer, don't run as quickly, and don't show mud splashes.

Tights are tights; find a brand that fits you and stock up in the January sales with enough to last for the next year.

I always wear stockings. Not only do men think they're sexy, but they fit better, and they're more economical! When one runs, there's still one left. Since most women buy tights, they've got cheaper. Stockings haven't. Elbeo and Aristoc both make Cantrece ones that don't wrinkle.

If you wear trousers all the time, you can either wear tights under them or knee-high socks. The socks have tight elastic tops, which make ugly rings around your calves, at least they do on mine.

Tights should fit properly or they'll drive you mad. Stockings should be small in the feet so they don't wrinkle at the instep and ankle, and long enough in the thigh so they don't cut into the fleshy part of your leg.

Jewellery

I'm not Lorelei Lee, and I don't believe diamonds are a girl's best friend; but a very basic decision you'll have to make for yourself is whether fabulous fakes are good enough for you, or if only the real thing will do.

I don't like costume jewellery; so I wear a few real things all the time, and forego the glitter.

Good jewellery adds a quiet touch of elegance to everything you wear. It's not as important that your companions know the gold is 14 carat as that you do, and the truth is that real is better.

Costume jewellery has become so expensive that if you succumbed to a number of amusing bits and pieces over a year, you'd have enough to pay for a skinny gold chain and a pair of pearl earrings.

Gilt turns black; enamel chips; beads break; jade shatters; and silver tarnishes. If you like earrings, get a pair of small gold hoops, and some cultured pearl buttons, medium size. That's all the Queen wears during the day, and you can bet she has an assortment to choose from.

The only fakes that can fool you are enamel bangles and earrings. Well done, the colours are good and true, skip the glitter settings, and let them shine on their own.

An engagement ring and wedding band are a lifetime decision. I am always sorry for the wives of successful men who still wear the tiny insignificant ring they got when they were young and he was just starting out. That ring belongs to the girl she was, not the woman she has become. I'd much rather have a zonking big semi-precious stone that carries some authority, than a perfect, but minuscule gem stone.

If Mr Right doesn't agree, or there is no money to spend on a frivolity like an engagement ring, I'd choose a very wide wedding band that couldn't be worn with any other ring anyway.

I love antique jewellery. The thought that something so unique has lasted hundreds of years, and that there's only one like it in the world, is very special. You can still pick up lots of Victorian and Georgian bargains in antique shops and markets. Lucky you.

Ear piercing is only for the brave as far as I'm concerned; but I did lose half a pair of the only valuable earrings I've ever owned, a diamond cluster, and from experience I can tell you there's not much you can do with one earring. I finally made mine into a ring. Not many alternatives.

Scarves

I had a theory in New York that before you could get promoted to Fashion Editor, you had to pass the Scarf Tie test. Me and my ten thumbs were not so hot at this; the future looked black. But then I went to work for Frances Patiky Stein, who was the most brilliant styling editor on any magazine. We'd have the most dreary little dress to photograph – no style – no interest, but big advertisers had to be kept happy, and Frances would do magic tricks with scarves, and I watched and I copied. Now I'm not great, but I'm almost good; all it takes is practice.

Learn to drape a cowl; twist a cowboy knot; fold a Beau Brummel ascot; pull a rectangular scarf through the loops and use it as a belt. Beg or borrow a man's long muffler, and knot it high under the collar on the outside of your coat.

Scarves don't have to be wildly expensive; cotton handkerchiefs from army surplus are super; but sleazy and sheer look horrible.

Skip spending money on an evening coat. Wrap yourself in an extra large scarf, or drape an embroidered fringed shawl like Carmen. Big is beautiful.

Hermès and Gucci pure silk squares are big; pretty enough to be an art form; and chic enough for Princess Anne to collect a wardrobe of them. Buy one a year; you'll keep them for ever.

They've got a label in them that says dry clean – but I wash all mine by hand in cold water and Woolite; then I iron them while they're still wet and not one has ever run. Honest Injun, at £35 I guess it can't afford to.

Fashion pages are always featuring clever tricks to tie a scarf so as to disguise disastrous hair-dos. I finally learned one, and that's my total repertoire. Fold a scarf into a triangle; pull it down

Four variations on scarf tying

across your forehead, and let the triangle end fall free at the back of your neck, while you knot the two ends in your hands on top of it. Roll a second scarf in a long narrow tube, and tie it around your head, at hairline level, for contrast. Tuck in the flapping end, or let it hang free. It's more practical to use a cotton square for this; silk slips.

Head Scarf Tying

Shoes

I've always had a passion for shoes, and I suffered agonizing misery as a child because my mother, quite rightly, insisted on horrifyingly ugly, lace-up styles, so that I'd grow up with good feet. Well, my feet are in fine shape, thank you; and my only extravagance now is expensive leather shoes.

I have bought cheap shoes, once! And I suffered excruciatingly, until I had worn them enough to feel less guilty about throwing them out. In a poll I did for the *Sunday Times*, every single fashion authority I questioned said that shoes and handbags were the first thing they noticed about a person's clothes.

I'd rather have one new pair of leather shoes a year for £40 than three pairs of High Street plastics. A cheap shoe is a cheap shoe. Good shoes are always a good buy in good sales.

If I had to, I could survive with three pairs of shoes, the rest are fashion dividends: one pair of good leather boots; one pair of black silk pumps; one pair of cream Chanel slingback pumps with a black toe.

At night I wear nothing but black silk ballet slippers on a half-inch heel. They cost £3.99 in the High Street, but in the Christmas sale they were reduced to £2.99, so I stockpiled four pairs, which should take me through 1981.

Never waste money on dying white shoes to match a particular evening dress. If black looks too chunky with light-coloured fabrics, get a pair of gold kid ballet slippers, the kind you find in hosiery departments.

Real ballet slippers are also available in most children's departments. Wear them with black tights for the Gigi look, with trousers, and as a substitute for bedroom slippers.

I used to spend money on summer shoes: beige and navy leather or black patent; but now I don't bother. Get cheap canvas espadrilles with a straw sole. Wear them to death, and then throw them out at the first sign of autumn leaves.

Rubber thong sandals. Woolworths always have them; one pair substitutes for bedroom slippers, which are a nuisance to get into, I always ruin mine by standing on the heels anyway. Wear them on holiday, rinse the sand away under the tap. Try them gardening, they keep the grubs away from your toes.

If you play tennis, buy one pair of plimsolls, white. They'll last for years.

Whatever shoe size you wear, don't try to squeeze into anything smaller; they'll hurt, it will show in your face. It's not worth it, honest. I have a solid bump on my right heel which came from breaking in a too small pair of Gucci moccasins in 1969. It would take plastic surgery to get rid of it now.

Outrageous shoes are never in; they just make exciting *Vogue* photographs.

Trademarks

A trademark is anything you wear so often over a year that you'd feel naked without it, and anyone who knows you well would notice it wasn't there.

I can't remember the last time I saw Deborah without her tiny diamond stud earrings; Penny without a skinny gold link bracelet; Grania without her gold wishbone ring; Linda without Frank's schoolboy watch; Lucinda without a gold L on a choker around her neck: Hilary without her Rolex watch; and even the pretty young Duchess of Gloucester always wears an 'R & B' brooch (her's and the Duke's initials). All trademarks.

Mine are four tiny rings, the Cartier gold rolling ring and three antique children's rings, with the world's smallest diamond chips, that I wear together on the little finger of my right hand; gold hoop earrings that I wear every day, and my leather-strapped Cartier wristwatch.

Trademarks

Choose anything you like: an antique brooch you inherited; an unusual belt buckle; earrings; rings; even a scent if you wear the same one all the time. Go through your jewellery box, and your accessory collection, and pick out three things, two of which you wear every single day.

Don't be a bit surprised if other women start copying you. Remember, imitation is the sincerest form of flattery.

Umbrellas

Used to be boring and functional. Now they come in smashing prints and colours. Considering how often we have to lug them around, prettiness is a big help.

Have two. One big one, plain wooden handle and attractive print, for the days it pours from morning to night. If it has got a wrist strap, cut it off. If it has got a shoulder strap, terrific! It leaves your hands free in between the showers. Also invest in a tiny telescopic one, which fits into a handbag and is perfect for travelling. I hated having to pay £7 for mine, but it has been money well spent, over and over again.

Watches

A necessity – something you can't get by without. The Cartier tank watch is the most famous design in the world, and although the original now costs £950 you'll be able to find a good gold-plated copy from about £25. Get it on a black leather strap, and wear it everywhere, except with evening clothes. Either don't wear any watch at all at night (I never do) or find yourself a small one on a gold strap that looks more like jewellery. A big sporty watch worn with delicate dresses looks worse than anything else I can think of.

Fancy little hanging watches, ring watches, watches in brooches – they're all terribly twee, and you won't want to know about them.

5 ✤ Caring For Your Clothes

Dry Cleaning and Washing

It's impossible to be well dressed if your clothes aren't clean and kept in perfect condition. Never put anything away if it needs to be washed, cleaned or repaired.

One of the most important relationships you will ever establish is with your dry cleaner. It may take you months of trial and error, but over a year, you'll have spent quite a sum with him, so he'd better play ball.

If you're in doubt about anything, dry clean, but as I take all my cleaning to one little local establishment I know Mary well enough to ask if it can be washed by hand, and I never have anything cleaned unnecessarily as it weakens the fabric.

I don't believe in spot cleaning for the amateur. You're working with chemicals and fragile fabrics, and it's just too big a risk. Choose a convenient cleaner, and let the professionals do it.

Always point out specific stains, and put a pin through them when you take them in, otherwise you may see them back again.

Cleaning problems also have a lot to do with the clothes you buy. I got the prettiest white wool dress from Annie Gough a few years ago, but after the first cleaning it was pale grey. I then discovered, to my cost, that dry cleaning spirits aren't white in the first place.

I wash by hand: cotton shirts and dresses; lingerie; French silk scarves; tee shirts; and all my woollies. The process is the same for all of them. Cold water, and 'Woolite' cold water wash. Leave to soak for five minutes, gently scrub and then rinse repeatedly till the water runs perfectly clear. Grubby water never got anything clean. I never put any of these things in a washing machine, as it's much too rough for them.

Don't put anything torn into a washing machine, as the tossing and turning will make it worse.

After washing sweaters, gently squeeze out excess water, gently pat into shape and then lay out flat on a turkish towel to dry. Don't hang them up, or they will pull out of shape; and don't let them get too near direct heat.

If shirt collars and cuffs have a dirt ring, rub shampoo into the marks before laundering. Shampoo's chemical formula is made to dissolve body oils.

If a zipper sticks after cleaning (always close when sending a garment to the cleaner) rub a little baby oil along one side of the zipper to lubricate it.

Any spot should be soaked, and then washed, in COLD water. Never ever soak or wash anything in hot water, or dirt and stains will be permanently set.

At regular intervals, wash your white nylon garments in Dylon Super White, according to the directions, to get rid of any grey tinge. Also use Dylon Super White if you scorch anything, but long term, be cautious as bleaching weakens all fabrics.

Ironing

Equipment:

A steam iron
An ironing board that can be adjusted to different heights
Washable ironing board cover
Clean cotton pressing cloth

Ironing is the only household chore I hate. The only compensation is to do it in front of the telly, or with the transistor blaring, not that it's much compensation.

A few years ago I went to see Estée Lauder in her palatial Eaton Square flat. I can't for the life of me remember how the subject ever came up, but she was horrified to hear I used a steam iron as she anxiously assured me it would take all the body out of any fabric. I was then marched into her blue bedroom, while we had a ten-minute dissertation and demonstration, which she did on a Dior dress, shaking me to my very soul; but here are her tips.

1 Make sure you know exactly what the fabric is, so you can set the iron's thermostat correctly.

2 Always iron on the wrong side, whatever the fabric, because ironing makes any material shiny.

3 If something has been washed, iron while it's still damp. Otherwise, use a damp pressing cloth, and press very hard.

4 Don't iron before putting clothes away. They'll just get cupboard creases.

5 Iron, and then wait five minutes before putting garment on; warm, damp fabric will more readily get out of shape.

6 Never put anything away damp. It may get mildewed.

7 With woollens, be sure you always have a cloth between the iron and the fabric.

8 Spray starch sticks to the iron, gets singed and comes off on the next thing you iron, with a nasty brown mark. Use starch carefully at the end of your ironing session. Then unplug the iron, leave it to cool completely and wash with a little scouring powder. Do it often so that it doesn't build up, but be sure to rinse well.

9 Never iron velvet, but steam it. Boil a kettle of water, and put on your oven gloves. When water has boiled, hold cloth over the spout, until the creases come out.

Shoe Care

The best way to ensure long life for good leather shoes and boots is to look after them.

1 Have the heels mended as soon as they are worn, and don't wait till the rubber heel is down to the leather.

2 Polish any colour with neutral wax, and buff well. Use coloured polish and you'll get dark marks rubbing off on your ankles. It's also more economical to use colourless polish, as it avoids lots of half empty tins with dried up wax in them.

3 Use spit and a rag to keep patent leather shining.

4 If black silk, or *peau de soie*, gets scuffed, go over the fabric with a cold wet sponge.

Basic Sewing Kit

I bought a small wicker sewing basket when I moved into my first flat, twelve years ago, and it has come around the world with me.

Contents:

Different size needles
Box of straight pins; special skinny ones if you sew silk fabric
Straight sharp scissors
Pinking shears
Tape measure
Reels of cotton: black and white, and any other colours that match
   your wardrobe
Hooks and eyes

Seam ripper

Seam ripper: my latest revolutionary discovery. It's a tiny sharp
   instrument which unpicks everything in seconds. It costs about
   45 pence at Singer shops
Safety pins, which I collect free from cleaner's tags

Sewing

I'm the most unco-ordinated woman you're ever likely to meet, but I find the simpler sorts of mending relaxing, and I do it in front of the telly.

Any real alterations, or clothes that need fitting, I have done by the magic Mrs Marsh; but I can make sure that buttons are securely on; hooks and eyes firmly in place; labels not hanging by a thread; coat linings in perfect condition. It's common sense that a stitch in time saves nine.

As long as hems are straight it's easy enough to turn them up, but shortening a crooked hem only produces a shorter, still crooked hem. On the other hand, lengthening any fabric is usually disastrous, and leaves a mark. What I did when skirt lengths dropped was to buy heavy upholstery braid and, after lengthening the skirt, I put on the braid to hide the mark. You can find a selection in most haberdashery departments. If a hem comes down at the eleventh hour, stitch it up even if the stitches are enormous, but don't use Copydex or any other glue, as you're then stuck for good.

My latest achievement is learning how to use a sewing machine. I was sent off to do a Home Sewing story for the *Daily Express*, and it took a morning's hard tutoring before I was able to sew a straight seam.

I bought the most simple Singer model, but one that has both the straight and zigzag stitches, which seems to cover every eventuality.

I'm not nearly good enough to make clothes for myself yet, but I've done dozens of things around the house: new bedroom curtains; sheets hemmed; cushions covered. The sewing machine is a lifetime investment that I think will pay for itself a dozen times over.

Don't buy a more complicated machine than suits your needs, and economize even further by waiting to buy your machine in a sale. Follow the instructions exactly. I sit with the extremely lucid booklet by my side and, so far, it has sorted out every problem as it arose. Do keep all the extra bits and pieces of equipment, even if you don't need them now; you might want them later.

If you enjoy sewing, and shudder at the price of clothes, it's worth investing in a proper sewing course. If the end result still turns out to have that 'Loving Hands At Home' look, forget it, but otherwise it's worthwhile learning the tricks of the trade, so that everything you make looks professional.

Make up simple designs in the best fabrics you can afford and, as an incentive, find yourself a corner just for sewing, with your machine permanently ready to use. Have enough space to lay out your fabric, even if it's the floor, or the bed, and be sure there's a good strong light.

Buttons

I started my button box when I was thirteen, and it's been with me ever since. I change the buttons on anything cheap, as tacky ones are the biggest give-away to chain store fashions It's astonishing the difference good ones can make, and they should always be as discreet and low key as possible. Anything garish is definitely not on.

Any nice buttons get put back in the button box when you get rid of clothes. They can be recycled time and time again.

Dyeing

If you mention 'little black dresses' to theatrical producer Frank Granat, he will be sure to regale you with the oft repeated story of Leslie's 'Widow's Winter'. I went to work for Frank while he produced a Noel Coward film; and I felt fat, poor and very, very bored with every single thing hanging in my cupboard, which I couldn't afford to replace. In a fit of genius I grabbed literally everything off the rail, took them to the corner cleaner and had them all dyed black.

The result was perfect, and I gaily trotted off to the office every morning, in yet another fetching little black outfit. Frank was very brave, and never mentioned what this sombre figure did to lower the level of gloom; but whenever I start pontificating on fashion he brings it up, and hasn't stopped teasing me about it to this day. I expect I did overdo it but, done in moderation, dyeing is terrific.

Dye faded nightgowns, shabby lingerie, odd stockings and old shirts. Synthetics don't take to a dye at all, but natural fabrics take perfectly. However, be warned; any colour dye will not cover the original colour. What it does do is combine with the shade already in the fabric. It takes a very deep strong colour to change completely what you start out with.

I swear by the Dylon products, but if you want to turn white bras and knickers flesh colour, try this trick. Brew up a very strong pot of tea, and add one tablespoon of salt. Let it go on simmering and drop in your clothes. Stir them around until they're slightly darker than the colour you want. Rinse in cold water and, afterwards, wash with a weak soap by hand.

Do:

Follow the printed instructions exactly
Wash the garment first
Wear plastic or rubber gloves, long enough to protect your arms
Remove any spots in advance, or they will come out a different colour
Stir constantly, and remove the garment from the dye according to instructions

Don't:

Dye any patterned fabrics
Dye any acrylic fabrics
Use too small a container, as the garment must be evenly covered and soaked
Wash them afterwards with anything but a detergent soap, or the colour will wash out

6 ✖ Organizing Your Fashion And Beauty Life

Storage Space

In order to put your clothes together to maximum advantage, you have to be able to see at a glance what you have to choose from. I copied the systems used in elegant couture establishments. If it's good enough for them, it's good enough for me.

I've got my cupboards organized so that there isn't an inch wasted, but at the same time I can see everything without an annoying search. The big trick is to make them pretty; paint them your favourite colour and cover the shelves with a contrasting washable contact paper. The size of the cupboard doesn't matter, it's what you do with it that counts.

With a little imagination nearly any house or flat will yield more storage space. Under the stairs, in corridors or room recesses, all are feasible, and behind inexpensive ready-made plywood doors, you can fit it out to your own specifications. I already had one roomy walk-in cupboard, but needed more. I decided to turn the small spare room into a dressing-room cum workroom for myself, and I've never regretted it.

I had the carpenter build three sets of cheap plywood doors, which together are the width of the room, nine feet. Two partitions went up to divide the space into three. The left-hand side has one high storage shelf and a rail six and a half feet off the ground. All my long dresses are kept here, along with the big plastic dress

79

bag in which I store out of season clothes. The right-hand cupboard has a high storage shelf, and a regular height rail which I use for coats and jackets, but is the correct height for men's suits. On the floor I stand up my boots. The centre cupboard has six shelves, and on these I keep all my clothes: nightgowns, scarves, belts, gloves, tee shirts, hats, boxes of stockings etc, which avoids having chests in the room, and gives me more wall space.

Inside the cupboards, I painted all the walls white, and the shelves, both top and bottom, are covered with a blue and white tile contact paper. I also covered the hanging rails and the floor with contact, so everything can be wiped down when I'm cleaning.

On the outside of the doors I put up a narrow fake moulding which I painted with eyeliner brushes in contrasting blue. I keep my sewing machine in here and, as a special convenience, I put a pretty floral print cover on the ironing board, and it stays out all the time, very handy for rush jobs.

Cleaning the Cupboards

The thought of cleaning out cupboards is loathsome to most people, but it's nearly as good as winning the Pools in my book. I have a passion for organizing – with everything exactly in place and all the corners evenly aligned. Probably extremely boring to live with, but oh so satisfactory to look at when you open the cupboard door.

Set aside a day, put on something scruffy and get started with your clothes cupboard first. Don't be in any rush as it's sure to take longer than you think.

Take every single thing out of the cupboard and throw it all on the bed.

Get into all the corners with the vacuum cleaner and dust all the shelves. Now, take a good look. Is the paintwork or wall paper clean? Is it your favourite colour? Are the shelves lined? Are there racks for your shoes? No? Then the first job is to make it every bit as pretty as your sitting-room. I painted every cupboard in my flat myself; they're low-ceilinged enough to need only a small step ladder, and small enough to finish in a couple of hours.

Use a high gloss, non-drip, water soluble, quick drying paint.

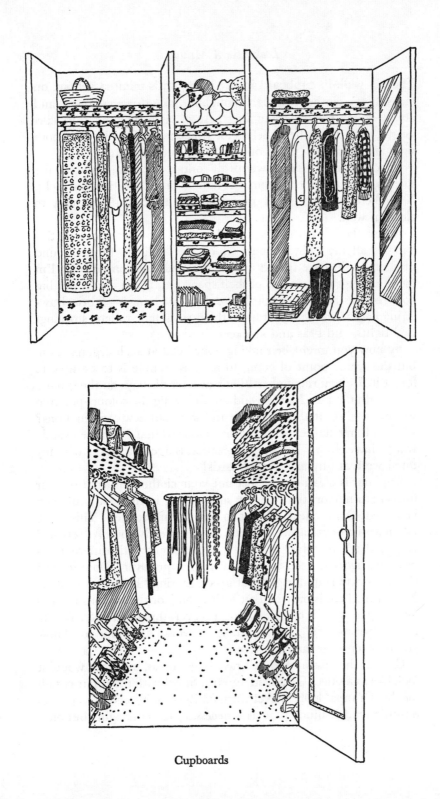

Cupboards

The big walk-in cupboard in my bedroom is mimosa yellow; on one side is a clothes rail high enough for long dressing gowns, and above it one shelf for handbags. Across is a hanging rail, skirt length, and above three shelves for sweaters. At floor level on both sides are shoe racks made out of skinny curtain rods.

I chose a big splashy flower print contact paper and covered the shelves, both top and bottom, the hanging rails and the shoe racks. Now the cupboard is not only smashing to look at, but easy to clean as well.

Across the back wall I attached a man's tie rack and from this dangles all my hair ribbons, which are as likely to go around presents as they are to end up on my head, and long chains. I'm lucky enough to have lots of shelf space but, if you don't, put big hooks on the inside of the cupboard door and hang big fabric drawstring bags from them to store bathing suits, hair rollers, stockings and tights, and bras and knickers.

By now you might be shaking your head at such organization, but the whole point of going to all this trouble is to be able to forget it. Do you remember Biba's sweater displays on the ground floor, with the merchandise laid out following the colour spectrum so you could see it all at a glance and work out new combinations? I keep all my clothes arranged by colour so that I can see exactly what I have. In my house, organization is freedom, and I wish my mind were as tidy as my cupboards!

Cupboards clean – now sort out your clothes. In front of your full-length mirror, try on every single thing in the vast jumble on your bed. Don't cheat, it's got to pass the mirror test. This is the moment for devastating honesty. Is it perfectly, purely, terrific? Right, that's the start of Pile 1. Experiment with different accessories. Does it need a scarf? a belt? a pullover? Does it need shoes? boots? Is it all right, but needs altering? Fine, that's Pile 2. Even if the hem is only half an inch wrong, or the buttons need to be changed, stick it on Pile 2. Pile 3 is everything you hate. Wrong colour, wrong size. Nothing makes it work. Anything you know you'll never wear ends up here.

Get out the scissors and be brave. Ugly dress, but what would it look like as a skirt? Go ahead and try. Shirts with the collar cut off for the 'Granpa' look. Jacket worn on its own, instead of as part of a suit. Spend as much time as is necessary to get it right; but once you've decided that something doesn't work, then it's Pile 3. Be strong, don't be sentimental.

Pile 3 is now your give-away heap. If you're lucky, you'll have a smaller friend who needs shorter skirts than you do. I had Lucinda who's not much over 5 feet, to my 5 feet 7 inches: and last summer we had a lovely clean out before she went for an Italian holiday, and she got some of my favourite dresses, including a never worn Jean Muir, and a scrumptious mint green Pauline Wynne Jones. With falling hemlines the dresses were much too knee-baring for me to get away with, so lucky Lu was in clover, and wearable clothes weren't wasted, hanging up unworn.

Pile 2 are the things that with alteration will have a new lease of life. Set them aside to get to work on. Back into the clean cupboard goes only those things that the critical eye in the mirror tells you are in perfect condition, and perfectly clean.

Have you found lots of things that are only to be worn in the summer and now there's snow on the ground, or vice versa? These things I store, in a big, see-through, plastic dress bag that holds about twenty-four garments. Twice a year I do my weeding; once for the hot weather, and then again for the cold. Always store things clean, either washed or dry cleaned depending on the material; but never have things altered at the end of the season. It really is a long, long time from May to September and proportions may have changed, your own as well as fashion's.

It has taken hours; you're exhausted; but it's done. If there are nice bits and pieces on discards, such as real leather belts or extra special buttons or scarves, I keep them. If you know they're worthwhile, but can't see a way to use them, then out. If anything is made of sensational fabric, save it to cut up for pot pourri sachets.

Every one of us has things hidden away which were always MISTAKES. Forget what they cost, forget their perfect condition, OUT. There's one big pile on the floor to be got rid of; another is on a chair to be altered; and a very small batch of clothes hang in the cupboard. That's terrific! And promise yourself that everything that goes into the cupboard from now on will be in mint condition. Really ready-to-wear.

Nearly as important as being well dressed is being well groomed, so make a habit of checking clothes as you take them off.

1   Anything that needs to be cleaned, washed or repaired I leave over the back of my bedroom chair. It annoys me so much to see it there that I rush to get the job done and put it away.

2   Always leave out clothes to air for half an hour when you take them off. Hang them in a draught, or near an open window.

3   Always hang clothes up with zippers closed and the top and bottom button done up, as it helps them to keep their shape.

4   Whatever their weight, shirts, sweaters and trousers are kept out all year, sub-divided by colour.

5   Hang coats separately from other clothes or they 'push'.

6   Coats should always be hung on heavy wide hangers that properly support the shoulders.

7   Never keep clothes on the wire hangers you get from cleaners. The hangers are so thin that they make a ridge in the shoulders. Buy proper hangers in a colour to go with your paint job. They last a lifetime.

8   Hang skirts on special hangers with clips or full-length press bars; never suspend them by hanging fabric loops, or they'll stretch to an uneven length, as well as getting badly wrinkled.

9   Anything cut on the bias, especially evening dresses, must not be hung, but kept folded flat on a shelf or in a big box, protected with tissue paper. If hung it'll get out of shape.

10   Keep belts hanging from a man's tie rack, or coiled on a shelf. Again, I keep mine grouped by colour on a shelf for easy co-ordination.

11   Keep boots standing upright; make a tube of either a piece of cardboard, or a rolled up magazine secured with a rubber band, and stick it down their length to keep them straight. Don't waste money on boot or shoe trees, which can stretch the leather away from the soles.

12   Keep handbags in a line on a shelf, not too squashed together. Store them closed to keep out dust and help them keep their shape.

13   For light items like ribbons and chains, screw two cup hooks into the wall, or back of the door. Stretch a string or

rubber band between the two hooks and hang things over it.
14 Make shoe racks from metal piping, or curtain rods, cut
to the width of the cupboard, and then covered with contact
paper. Screw in two rods, an inch and a half apart, on the
slant, so the heel hooks over the top one, and the shoe sole
rests on the other one. Look at every pair of shoes; does it
need to be reheeled? repaired? Give away any that are too
shabby to care about.

15 Hang trousers on a trouser hanger; and if there is meant
to be a crease, keep them folded that way.

16 Be sure you have a proper light; the whole point is to be
able to match colours quickly, and be able to find things.

17 If your cupboard is very tiny; keep all your clothes in
plastic cleaner's bags so they slot in and out more easily;
otherwise remove these bags when you bring things back from
the cleaners. Dust adheres to plastic.

18 On a two-door cupboard, arrange mirrors so that you
can see both your front and back.

19 Get plastic hat dummies at Woolworths. Wrap each hat
in a cleaner's plastic dress bag to protect against the dust.
Two or three hats can go on each stand as long as they are not
pressed tightly together.

20 If moths are a problem in your climate, buy mothballs
and keep them in an open jar behind your jumpers. I never
bother.

21 Padded hangers are best for any thin fabric. Be sure the
slope of the hanger fits the slope of your clothes' shoulders.
There are lots of different styles around, so you'll have no
trouble finding one that suits the specific garment.

22 No matter how neatly you keep beads and chains, they'll
tangle in a drawer or on a shelf. Screw big hooks into the wall
and suspend them.

23 Keep little jars of pot pourri on all the shelves.

24 If you've got drawers, line them with a pretty paper or
even a printed cotton that you attach in the four corners with
a staple gun. Again I swear by contact paper. Sachets are
scrumptious; they make clean clothes seem even cleaner.

Pot Pourris

I get a feeling of great luxury when I walk into a cupboard, or open a drawer, and the subtle scent of pot pourri wafts up. It evokes hundreds of memories: hot summer days in Oxfordshire; first spring blossoms in the south of France, Scottish heather in August.

Now that I've learned to make my own, it's only a question of pennies to keep everything smelling fresh year round.

There are many traditional recipes, but I mix any flowers that come my way: roses when I'm spoilt by a generous beau; geraniums from the sitting-room window boxes; lavender from Lavinia's farm in Berkshire.

1 Lay all the flowers to dry in a single layer on a tray. Leave them in any warm place and turn over occasionally until they are crumbly. The flowers are completely dry when the petals fall off the stalks as you shake them. Rose petals hold their shape so you can leave the flower whole.

2 Heap the mixture in pretty bowls; ones with wide necks give out a stronger scent. Add a teaspoon of orris root powder to each container and mix through. The powder helps preserve the scent and the colour.

When I'm feeling extravagant I add the ends of bottles of scent, or bath oil, to the mixture and give it a new lease of life. A good stirring revives it miraculously. Experiment with different colours and scents until you find the one that especially pleases you.

Make small fabric sachets by cutting out two pieces of fabric, 3 × 5 inches; sew them together along two long and one short side, inside out. Turn them right side out, fill them with pot pourri mixture and tie up the top with a scrap of ribbon. These I stick in every drawer in the house. When their smell begins to be faint, I just pour scent on them and put them back, making sure the damp side doesn't touch any clothing or it will leave a stain.

Dressing Table

When I was a little girl growing up in New York City, I was convinced that if only I had a dressing table it would turn me from a pumpkin into a Princess.

It was 1971, and London, before I ever got that dressing table; it was an £8 bargain and it was well worth the wait. All those endless years of making up my face in the steamy bathroom, when I could have been ensconced before my miniature laboratory.

Again the key is organization. It may take time to set up properly, but once done it's going to last for life. My table has a flat centre drawer which I have divided into four sections with pretty boxes that originally came as cosmetic company packaging.

Back left: manicure equipment
Back right: hair clips, slides, barrettes
Front left: the face make-up I use on a daily basis
Front right: the eye make-up I use on a daily basis

On either side are two very deep drawers, and I have fitted the left one out as my make-up store cupboard. Last year Clinique did a big beauty promotion with miniature products packed in clear plastic containers. Over the six months that the special offer was on, I collected six of them, and each is large enough to hold about eight blusher or eye shadow cases, or twelve lipglosses.

I'm spoilt by getting beauty samples which cosmetic companies want me to write about. Those I like I keep, but experience has taught me to give away any I'm sure I'll never use. I know, when I sit down to do my face in a rush, that everything is at hand and accessible. Even though the dressing table sits at right-angles to the window, and is well lit during the day, I always keep the lamp lit to do my face, since that's the light any face is usually seen in. In addition to a three-way table-top mirror, which I can angle as I like, I always work with a small revolving mirror; normal one side, magnifying the other. The surface is large enough for me to lay out all my equipment, and spills and stains are easily wiped off.

Bathrooms

Do scientists work in dark, scruffy, uncomfortable laboratories? No, then why should we? The bathroom in my flat was dark and dour; an enchanting French, flower printed paper went up on the walls: I made curtains from matching fabric, and had the odd-job man build a cupboard, with a shelf, around the basin. Not only does it hide all those ugly pipes, but it also eliminates the need for a wall cabinet to put jars and bottles in. Tag ends of wall paper cover the plywood cupboard, and I also stuck it on to the sides of the bath, making the room's three-foot width seem much more spacious.

Ultimate luxury is a deep pile shaggy carpet on the floor. Gloriously cosy at all times, it came as a remnant in a sale and was extremely cheap. I've never had a catastrophic spill; it doesn't get splashed from the bath; and cold clammy lino would be purgatory at 7 a.m.

I never do my face in there, so I didn't worry about an expensive light at mirror level; instead I make do with only a ceiling fixture. If you need a shower curtain, and can't find a pretty waterproof one, make your own from a smashing printed sheet, and line it with a clear plastic curtain. It's easy and cheap to do.

The basin cupboard is three feet long, so there's plenty of storage space. On the bath's splashback ledge I keep any pretty small scent bottles, and on the counter top only a tumbler, tissue box and cotton wool kept in a decorative jar. Incidentally, never waste money on pre-shaped cotton balls. Buy the big surgical rolls which are always in the post-Christmas sales. I find one lasts a year, and they are a fraction of the cost of all those multi-coloured packs.

Bathroom Equipment I can't live without

Vidal Sassoon Shampoo
Vidal Sassoon Finishing Rinse
Pumice stone
Razor
Shaving Cream
Mitchum's Anti-perspirant
Bath Oil
Toothbrush
Toothpaste
Body Lotion
Sponge
Buf-Puf
Cleansing Oil
Clarifying Lotion

Eye Make-up Remover
Scrub Cream
Facial Soap
Roger & Gallet Carnation bathsoap (when it's in my Christmas
  stocking) otherwise hotel samples or supermarket specials

Your cupboards, dressing table and bathroom cabinets are all
spotlessly clean now, and you won't put one thing back that isn't
totally great, and isn't in perfect condition. Promise!

7 ❧ Looking After Your Looks

Skin Care

I passionately desire poreless skin, a flat stomach and skinny thighs; and if I were named Faust instead of Field, I would have sold my soul years ago to the devil, even if I only got two out of my three desires.

They are all gifts of the gods; and none more so than a good skin, because a flawless skin is nearly one hundred per cent hereditary. If your mother had large pores, or a problem complexion, you probably will also. It is also true that a great many skin problems are temporary, and most of them can be controlled.

Good skin is largely self-discipline; nothing will work for you if you only do it now and then. Whatever you have to do for a clear complexion, you have to do all the time. Every child in the world has a fresh skin, and they're never too young to be taught how to keep it that way. Skin types never change; but what can change is the condition: wrinkles, dryness, oiliness, flaking, texture, which is why it's so desperately important that you do what is best for you.

The one thing I don't begrudge money spent on is skin care – after all my skin is the only one I've got, and it's going to last me for a lifetime.

That said, I must have tried a dozen different beauty regimes before I discovered Clinique, which gives me as good-looking a skin as I am naturally capable of having. The products are hypoallergenic, meaning they are fragrance free and mild, which has to be good for anyone, even if they don't happen to have a particular allergy.

The important thing is to find things that work, and a system that you'll follow. There's no rule that says the only things that work are the most expensive; but if you like a costly brand, buy enough in the January and July sales to take you through the next six months.

I think the current vogue for home-made treatment products is silly. It takes valuable time to make up the creams and lotions; the natural ingredients are expensive; and since skin specialists know what they're doing, why should I bother to compete with them?

Skin Types

It's important to know your skin type; get it wrong and the products you use may turn out to be useless. Everyone has some oiliness around the nose, but the forehead, cheek and chin areas are more difficult to judge by just looking.
Use this tissue paper test to check your type.

1 Cut out three pieces of tissue paper, or you can substitute unused cigarette papers. Each one should be about two inches square. Mark them 1, 2 and 3.
2 Clean your face thoroughly and use a mild skin tonic. Don't touch your face for one hour.
3 Wipe paper 1 across your forehead.
4 Wipe paper 2 across your nose, mouth and chin.
5 Paper 3 goes across your cheeks.

If the paper remained unmarked, the skin is dry in that area. If the paper picks up slight moisture but glides across the skin, it is normal. If the paper shows traces of grease and adheres, that area is oily. Most skins are a combination, oily spots in some areas, dry in others.

Normal skin: If you've got no dry flaky patches and no oily areas either, your sebaceous glands are producing the perfect amount of oil. Cleanse, wash, moisturize and thank your lucky stars.

Combination skin has a greasy T zone down the forehead, nose and chin, which starts to shine three to four hours after make-up is applied, but the cheek area is dry. You have to look after the two different types of skin you have separately. Use your skin tonic more often on the T zone than on your cheeks. Use a face scrub on your face twice a week, but if necessary use it extra on the T zone. Before you go to sleep, put extra moisturizer on your cheeks.

Dry skin is fine textured and looks slightly stretched. It may get flaky after you wash it, burnt in the sun and chapped in the cold. It shows the first lines and wrinkles much more quickly than a skin with enough oil to plump it out.

In the morning, wash with mild soap and warm water. Apply moisturizer while your skin is still faintly damp. At night, remove make-up with removal cream, then wash as in the morning. To apply your skin tonic, lightly wet cotton wool with water, pour skin tonic on to the damp cotton, then gently dab it on your face. Rinse off with cool water, then apply moisturizer.

To get rid of the flaky skin, use a Buf-Puf when you wash, and frequently reapply your moisturizer. If you use too much under your foundation it will be splotchy and streaky, so go easy, but put on an extra thick coat before you go to sleep.

Oily skin may seem a disaster when you're sixteen, with a shiny nose, blackheads and a propensity to spots; but at fifty you'll be thrilled that you have fewer wrinkles than your dry-skinned friends. At least that's what I keep telling myself.

In the morning, wash with soap and water. Apply skin tonic with cotton wool, rinse your face and apply a light moisturizer. Before you go to bed, remove your make-up, wash again and apply a very tiny amount of moisturizer. The biggest problem for you is that your nose and forehead begin to get shiny an hour after you've put on your make-up. During the day, or before dressing for dinner, you may have to remove your make-up with cleansing oil, wash again as in the morning and reapply moisturizer.

My skin care programme is three products, three minutes, three times a day. How can you find anything to complain about when it is as simple as that? Because I am often sent samples of new products I have tried various other systems on my face, but either I didn't think my skin looked as good and smooth and soft or they weren't as easy to use, so for nearly five years I've stuck to what works best for me.

The head of Clinique is a tall dynamic former Beauty Editor whom I first met at *Vogue*. Carol Phillips is now a grandmother: but when I see her on trips back to New York I can't see any evidence that she's a day older than she was when I first saw her rushing down Condé Nast corridors.

You may have to experiment for a few months before you find products that make a visible difference, but what's a few months when you'll want your skin to look good for years?

1 Don't use any baby products on your face. They're far too rich and greasy for an adult skin. At some time or another, you're sure to buy a cream that's a mistake and your skin will be quick to tell you so. Don't throw it out, but don't go on applying it to your face; instead use it as a body lotion.

2 If you live in a hot climate, keep any alcohol-based product in the refrigerator so that it not only cleanses, but cools as well.

3 Always apply cleansing products in upward rotating motions. This helps them to get into the pores.

4 If your skin develops a muddy, stodgy look, try a facial mask. It increases the circulation and acts as a deep cleanser. Although they are only temporary, some of them are specially formulated to plump out the tiny lines that run between your chin and nose. Try one before a big night out.

5 It's easy to forget how much wax builds up in ears. Too much can lead to blackheads in the ears, but it can also affect your hearing, so use a cotton bud to clean every morning. Never use any sharp instrument.

6 Don't use a fancy scented soap on your face. Choose a plain complexion soap. Be sure you remove every last trace, or you'll find it itchy; water is the first stage of moisturizing anyway.

7 The outer layer of skin that we actually see is made up of dead cells, which get replaced by a new layer from underneath. If they aren't removed when you clean your face, your complexion will look muddy instead of sparkling. To help get rid of them, use a Buf-Puf, a man-made fibre sponge, like a pot scourer, which speeds up the exfoliating process.

8 When we're in an emotional state it can affect our skin:

and experts agree that stress and tension can trigger off spots, or allergies such as hives.

9 On the rare occasions I apply a face mask, usually if I've been given a sample, as I'm too mean to buy one, I use it before a big evening, and lie back in a warm bath for a rest while it's working.

10 Strong astringents do dry up the oiliness, but the oil glands, just to be helpful, work overtime and you set up a wicked cycle.

11 There are two schools of thought about whether your skin will eventually get so used to a routine that it stops working. I find that when the weather goes from hot to cold, or vice versa, my skin shows the difference for a few weeks by becoming either very flaky or very oily. I vary my regime till it evens out, but I don't switch brands.

Skin Cleansing

There are two schools of cleansing: the milk and cream school, or the soap and water school. Do what suits you best.

1 Always cleanse your face in the morning. I was once accosted, after doing a television programme on beauty and fashion in Belfast, by a woman who said she never cleaned her face when she got up, as there was nothing to get it dirty in the night! Quite untrue; there's plenty of grime in the air, and your skin has expelled oil during the night. In the morning I use soap and water, quick, no big scrub.

2 To redo my face during the day, I always start from scratch. Soap and water won't dissolve the oil-based ingredients of make-up, so I massage in cleansing oil with my fingers before I tissue it off. Next comes the soap and water stage, and after getting a good sudsing going, I scrub, in upward circular motions, with my Buf-Puf. I then wipe off the lather with a natural sponge and splash water on my face. I pat dry, apply skin tonic with cotton wool and, from personal preference, I rinse this off as well before drying and applying moisturizer.

3 I repeat my cleansing regime before I go to bed, and three

days a week I use the 7th-Day Scrub Cream, which has thousands of gritty particles in it. Never, ever, do I go to bed with my make-up on. I used to (not often) and the next morning, even after washing, my complexion still looked muddy.

Toners

The second cleansing step not only tightens up the pores, but helps with the exfoliating process. All toners are spirit-based and leave your skin feeling a little tingly.

1   Saturate a wad of cotton wool with astringent, and gently draw it across your face in an upward sweep, including your hairline, neck and behind your ears. Delicately go in under the eyes, but never on the very thin skin at the corners of your eyes, or on your eyelids. Use it on the fold of skin under the brow which can get dried out and flaky. If at the end the cotton is grimy, repeat the process. Then splash your face with cool water before patting it dry and putting on moisturizer.
2   If I skip the cleansing oil and just wash my face, a lot of make-up is left to be removed by the tonic. So much of what we put on our faces isn't water soluble that it's no economy to skip a make-up remover.

Moisturizer

No skin of any type can survive without moisturizer. This is just as true for oily skin as dry, because moisturizer not only lubricates the skin, but equalizes the oily and dry patches which we all have. If you put on foundation without a base coat of moisturizer, it runs on the oily spots, and flakes on the dry.

If you've got such a good complexion that you don't need foundation, it's even more important that you protect your skin from dust and the elements with moisturizer.

1   After cleaning your face well, apply the smallest possible amount of moisturizer on slightly damp skin which helps it to be quickly absorbed. I let it sink in while I'm doing my eyes,

about five minutes, and then I gently blot it with a tissue before I put on foundation.

2 I use my moisturizer as a night cream as well; anything heavier or more oily causes spots to appear, and a greasy face doesn't encourage a stimulating love life either.

3 At least once a day, moisturize your neck and throat. Dab some on the base, and then work it in, in gentle upward strokes.

4 Use your moisturizer on the chest as well. This area is padded with oil glands, so if you're prone to spots, they're as likely to appear here as on your face, and most body creams are too rich.

5 Put moisturizer on your lips when you're not going to apply lipstick or gloss. It keeps them smooth and supple. Never use it under a regular lipstick, as it makes the colour bleed into the little lines that radiate out from your lips.

6 Especially in the summer, when you perspire more, drink lots of water to replace the moisture your body is losing.

7 When you fly, put on an extra coat of moisturizer once you're in your seat. Pressurized cabin air is so dry that you can literally feel your skin crack. Before you land, wash your face and put on fresh moisturizer and foundation.

8 In the summer use moisturizer more often; it gets washed away either internally, from perspiration, or externally, from heat and sun, and needs to be replaced.

9 Dry heat makes make-up penetrate the skin more deeply, so if you're somewhere with lots of central heating, never skip your moisturizer.

10 Cheap tip: next time you prepare avocados for a meal, save the skin and wrap it in a plastic bag until you're ready for your bath. Smooth the inside on your clean face, and soak in a warm bath. It's full of polyunsaturated fats that are terrific for your skin.

11 I am opposed to anyone using hormone creams. Besides being horribly expensive, some friends have reported that they appear to encourage hair growth, and who needs that? More important, some doctors believe they are a cancer risk. They can upset the metabolism of your skin and, like a drug addiction, having plumped up the skin cells, you need to keep feeding them, because they're hooked.

Estée Lauder has no patience with any woman who complains moisturizer is an expensive luxury. 'Ridiculous,' she admonished me. 'You need so little that even a small jar lasts for ever.' She also told me that an older woman shouldn't suddenly switch to a heavier cream because she's had another birthday, instead, she should lubricate more often.

Make-up

If I'd been alive one hundred years ago, I'd have been in dead trouble. Nice girls didn't, couldn't, use cosmetics, but thank goodness, today, we can all gild the lily with no fear of censure.

Even at the luxury end of the market, the amount you spend on a product is so small that if you've made a dreadful mistake you won't have wrecked the family budget for the month. There's only one test make-up has to pass as far as I'm concerned, and that's 'Does it work for me?' The Queen of England and Jackie Onassis both use Cyclax but it doesn't suit me. Princess Anne likes navy-blue mascara, but it makes me look as if I've got a hangover. The only expert you need to worry about is you.

Lots of men say 'I don't like my wife to wear make-up,' but what I think is bothering them is that it's not put on well, and looks too contrived. If you want some expert personal help, go to the best local beauty salon.

My friend Nancy came up from Torquay to London last year especially to have a make-up session at Joan Price's Face Place and she was delighted with the results, as was her husband David. At thirty-four, with two school-age children, she wanted a more sophisticated look that suited her life, yet was easy to apply. There are so many products on the market that it's difficult to know what's right for you, and it's ultimately a question of trial and error, but at least professionals can offer some shortcuts.

My goal is to look good all day long, and my make-up is the same night and day, indoors and outdoors. I may use less or more depending on circumstances, but if I need make-up, and I do, I need it all the time, and anywhere I go. I've been the guinea pig for two major make-overs: the first when I was twenty for *Glamour*, and the second when I was thirty for the *Sunday Times*. I had the benefit of the best experts showing me what to do, but it took practice for me to do it myself.

With every year, your face is supposed to take four minutes longer to do. It may be true that I spend more time now, but in fact I'm using less make-up, and with a much lighter hand. Heavy make-up exaggerates faults and hides assets. The only thing to remember when you begin to experiment is that old habits are the natural enemies of a new look.

Copying a magazine photograph can be a big help. Last year the thumb print effect of smudged eye shadow was big, and I learned how to get the effect from a picture of Pauline Stone in *Woman's Journal*. How far in towards the centre of my face should the blusher go? Do I want it right on the ball of the cheek? *The Vogue Beauty Book* gave me the answer to that one. Eyeliner underneath the lower lashes? Jean Shrimpton just used dots of colour in a David Bailey photograph, and now so do I. Gleam under the brow bone? It suits Princess Grace, and it suits me too.

Make-up should have one function only, and that is to make you look good enough to forget about your looks. Make your beauty regime automatic and it will go quickly.

1 Buy small sizes: this way, when a new product appears, you won't feel guilty at having lots of half-finished bottles left. I also find that almost all liquid products dry up to some extent, and colours look jaded after a while, so for me small is beautiful. Hoarding also means you'll be frugal with how much you use; remember, it's easy to add more if it's needed, it's murder to have to take off without starting from scratch.
2 We see a face the way we read a page, starting at the upper left-hand corner. The trick is to provide enough interest, so that the gaze doesn't travel from eyebrow to nose, off to the cheek and out of the face. Centre attention on the planes that climb upwards. Style your make-up and hair so that as the force of gravity pulls your face down, you deliberately give the impression of an upward lift.
3 The shape and lines of your face have to have contrast. If you have a round face, with round eyes and small features, you need a divergent line somewhere, so leave your eyebrows

straight and don't arch them. If your face is angular, then balance it with rounded mouth, cheeks or eyes.

4 Start with a scrubbed, clean face, not only will it show if you don't, but your skin will eventually pay the price.

5 Always put your make-up on in clear bright light. I prefer to do it by electric light, but then, during the day, I check it in the natural light to make sure it's not overdone.

6 I always look prettier at night, and strangely enough it's not just the light; the quality of my skin is better, the make-up lasts longer and looks better. Electric lights are supposed to deaden the complexion, and rub out colour, but I don't think it's true, not if you take that into account as you make up.

7 Avoid too bright a look at any time; in the summer when I'm tanned I try to look more rosy, and in the winter I wear bolder, deeper eye and lip shades to balance the winter gloom. In both cases I want my teeth and eyes to stand out as white and bright.

Scent

I have a passion for scent, which makes me feel good as well as smell good. According to Coco Chanel, our sense of smell is the only one of our senses that is still instinctive, and lives on nostalgia and our subconscious. She always quoted Paul Valéry's aphorism as her motto, 'a woman who doesn't use perfume has no future'.

Perfume doesn't necessarily make you sexy, but I do think you can hypnotize a man with it, and I can't see the point of choosing one that is so expensive you have to use it sparingly. Spray it, splash it, use it lavishly, or where's the pleasure in it? Fragrance changes from woman to woman, and something you like on a friend may smell completely different on you. You may want to wear a lighter scent during the day, something heavier and more exotic at night.

In the summer when it's hot and sticky I choose something more citrousy, or a man's cologne like Dior's Eau Sauvage, Paco Rabanne or Trumper's Lemon.

I often get scent samples at fashion shows, or press lunches, but I've always wanted enough money to wear one scent all the time and after a while it would be instantly recognizable to everyone who knows me.

There's been a revived interest in distinctive bottles the last few years, and I keep the prettiest ones, such as Chloë, Youth Dew or Private Collection, even when they're empty. I discovered Givenchy III when a delicious man gave it to me a few years ago. Sophisticated and tangy, it also has a marvellous second kick which always reminds me of the sensation you get from smelling fine brandy. Nicest of all for frugal me, is the plexiglass cylinder the bottle comes in, which I use as a bedside pencil container.

Trumper's Lemon was King Edward VII's favourite, I borrowed it from a loved one years ago, and it's my first choice for a cool summer reviver. Another gift was Calandre, and it's joined my list of special goodies. One of the most unusual I've worn is Aromatic Elixirs by Clinique. It comes in smoky brown bottles, like old-fashioned apothecary jars, and is supposed to last for twenty-four hours, during which time it changes and adapts to the rhythm of your body. Nice, and I get more comments when I wear it than with any other scent.

As you can see, my pet scents have an emotional attachment which I think is true for most women. Disastrously, I've got a very weak sense of smell as I suffer from hayfever, so I use a lot, and hope no one in the vicinity will faint. I keep small samples for my purse, and reckon that after a maximum of four hours another spray is needed.

1 Put on any fragrance while you are still slightly damp from the bath; this makes the scent take better and last longer.
2 Never spray with jewellery on, as perfume will discolour pearls, and cause black spots on gold.
3 I use scent behind my ears, between my breasts and on the inside skin of my wrists and arms. I don't get it on my face or my hair, and I try to keep it away from clothes. After a few minutes I always buff these areas with my hands so that it doesn't sit on the skin surface and stain fabrics.
4 Don't open a new bottle until you're ready to start using it. Perfume will evaporate and even change when exposed to the air.
5 If you have very dry skin, try perfume oils as they contain

no alcohol. Take special care though, as they rub off on fabric and stain. Oils also linger longer than perfume or cologne.

6   It's a waste to pour perfume in the bath. It gives no smell at all because the alcohol drowns without a trace. Do use bath oils which leave your skin feeling like satin, in addition to the delicious smell.

7   There's no point in lots of scents fighting, so either choose matching deodorant, talcum powder and perfume; or use unscented deodorant and talc, and leave all the smell to your scent.

8   Be careful about wearing perfume in the sun. In addition to their alcohol base, which is drying to the skin, many of them have ingredients like Oil of Bergamot, which can cause brown skin blotches from the reaction of certain chemicals to the sun.

Acne

The most important thing to know about acne is that there have been enormous medical strides forward in the past few years, and it's no longer necessary for anyone to suffer from it.

A course of antibiotics, working directly on the grease gland, stops the pores from getting blocked and inflamed, so that the spots are cleaned up from within, where they start.

Interestingly enough, there is evidence that acne, along with oily skin and a tendency to baldness, is inherited. Acne can occur at any age, not just the teenage years, and most doctors now agree that chocolates and fried foods have a great deal less to do with it than we once thought. Close to 80 per cent of the population suffer from spots at some time in their lives; but if yours are more than the occasional pimple, and if they are either constant or constantly recurring, hie yourself to the nearest dermatologist, and if he doesn't help, find another; different doctors have different remedies.

The dictionary definition of acne is: 'a chronic inflammatory disease of the skin'. One of the factors causing it is a dysfunction of the endocrine glands which secrete hormones into the blood stream. The normal function of one of these, progesterone, is to act on the oil glands keeping your skin supple and moist.

If your hormones get out of hand, however, the oil glands on your face, chest and back are overstimulated, become clogged, then inflamed, and erupt. All very unattractive.

I think it's impossible to look clean if you have blackheads, although they're not, contrary to superstition, dirt. The blackhead is the final process of a spot of dried up oil which has been exposed to the air. That's why you can't get rid of it just by a good washing. It has to be cleaned out down deep.

Oil gets clogged at the follicle opening if the pore is not kept clean; or the horny layer may produce cells faster than the cells are drying and shedding, so that the follicle opening is blocked and the oil can't get out. I found the two best products to solve this particular problem are a Buf-Puf and a face scrub. Both of them provide enough friction to remove that flaky, messy-looking, top layer of skin. After washing your face with a Buf-Puf, put on moisturizer and your skin will already feel softer.

Most acne clears up, but even after the spots are gone, you may have enlarged pores and a slightly splotchy complexion. If you have bad acne scars, you can have dermabrasion: a stiff rotary brush planes down the surface of your skin until it has reached the depth of your pit marks. At first your face will look red and puffy, but then the skin will return to normal and be a great deal smoother than it was before. This particular operation can only be done after all infection and inflammation are gone, and must be done by a doctor or dermatologist.

Although every expert tells us not to, most of us pick at pimples. I know myself well enough to know I'll never stop, so at least I try to do it under as ideal conditions as possible.

I clean my face as usual, and then I fill the basin with boiling water: if yours doesn't get hot enough, boil the kettle. When it is really steaming, bend over and cover your head with a towel so that no steam can escape. Give your face a sauna for about three minutes which is sufficient to open the pores; any longer and I'm gasping for breath. I then scrub my hands and sit in front of the magnifying mirror on my dressing table which is well lit. After I go through the revolting, but soul satisfying, process of squeezing any blackheads which the heat has softened, I wash my face again, splash it with cold water to close up the pores, and then dab on face lotion with cotton wool.

To clear up any bad spot as quickly as possible, dry it out, doing it very carefully so that the surrounding skin doesn't get flaky as well. The most effective thing I've found is a liquid soap called pHisoHex. After washing and drying your face, dab pHisoHex on the spot, reapplying it every few hours. Overnight is usually long enough to defuse it.

Whenever you have a bad pimple, try to leave all make-up off as it tends to aggravate the problem. If you have to look good, put on your make-up as normal, use an extra dab on the blemish and then powder the spot well so that no light reflects off your skin and makes it more noticeable.

You may find your skin looks much better in the summer; Vitamin D builds up from sunlight and helps to clear up complexions.

I often find that with the outbreak of cold weather, as I start wearing heavy woollen pullovers, I get a slight outbreak of pimples on my back and upper arms. It has to do with the oil glands having no room to breathe, so I keep after these areas with a strong skin tonic which quickly dries them out.

Most of the acne treatments you can get at the chemists are technically known as 'kevatalitics', and they take off the top layer of skin and dry out the inflammation. Vitamin C can help your skin, and so can Yeast tablets which are rich in Vitamin B.

If you get spots only on your forehead, it may be that you have an oily scalp and your oily hair touching your skin is causing the trouble. Use astringent on cotton wool along your hairline every time you wash your face. Also, clean the skin behind your ears, and along your hairline with skin tonic as it gets very oily.

If you're not getting all the shampoo out of your hair, you may also get an allergetic rash or pimples. I never sleep with my fringe falling on my forehead, but hold it back with a band, so that there is that much less chance of dirt and oil settling on my skin.

If you have very fair skin, you may be able to see little red spots. These are usually burst capillaries, and can be removed by a dermatologist with an electric needle. The sensation is like having an injection, but it quickly disappears.

Cancer

Whatever our skin type, most of us have some freckles, small brown flat spots, which come from unevenly distributed flecks of pigment in the epidermis. Other brown marks, usually slightly raised, and to the feel a little bumpy under the skin, are birthmarks, and have no special significance unless their appearance changes. If they are large enough to be unsightly, and you are bothered by them, they can be removed under a local anaesthetic, and you are left with a tiny scar that looks like the mark you get from a vaccination.

I was born with dozens of these birthmarks; it never even occurred to me that everyone else didn't have them as well. When I was seventeen, I needed a long white dress for a dance, and found the most beautiful gown at New York's most elegant department store. Heavy ribbed silk, utterly plain, it had a high front, very demure, but a deep low scoop back which I thought the acme of sophistication and sex appeal.

I chose it all on my own, a terrific responsibility I thought, but my mother came along to a fitting, and saw a birthmark on my back that she said looked 'not very pretty', so why didn't I have it taken off for cosmetic purposes?

I couldn't even see it, but I trotted off like a good girl. In fact, the reason it looked odd was because it had turned malignant, and I had cancer. It's surprising how difficult it is even to write that word: it's associated with so much superstition and fear. After the first minor operation, there was another major one, and then twenty-four hours later, a big teddy bear of a surgeon, whom I adored, unwrapped the twenty pounds of pressure bandages to show off the results, and I was faced with the enormity of what had happened to me.

The original birthmark was perhaps the size of a sixpence, certainly not much larger, and so I thought the scar might be the size of a 50 pence piece; but of course, in order to make sure they'd got rid of the entire malignancy, they'd had to remove all the nerves and tissue in the centre of my back, so that the scar went across its width, and up and down. To my horrified eyes, it looked like a bloody side of beef hanging in the butchers.

The medical facts had nothing to do with my reaction. I wasn't in the least bit grateful for being alive; I was far too furious at God for allowing this to happen to me. I hated him; I hated the world; and I hated my body which had let me down so badly.

I wasn't very different, I expect, from any other woman who has to fight an illness, not only for its medical significance, but also for its cosmetic ramifications. Since that first operation there have been others, but none left such a bad scar. I still can't bear the sight of my back, but the area the scar covers is so large that although cosmetic surgery might have been able to make a neater scar, it wouldn't have left me much less marked.

I couldn't say honestly to anyone that a scar isn't a traumatic experience. For a very long time I had a grudge against the world, but eventually I came to terms with it, even if I never forget it. Oddly enough, being so ill has had surprisingly little effect on what I've done with my life.

For ten years after I had cancer I wore a motley assortment of bathing suits that were more suitable to Margaret Rutherford than a twenty-year-old girl; but they were the only things I could find to hide my scar. I finally got up the courage to bare my back and wear a maillot but I still won't wear an evening dress that reveals my back.

Plastic Surgery

The most painful, and expensive, beauty decision you'll ever be called on to make is whether you are so bothered by some feature, or the first signs of advancing age, that you decide to have plastic surgery. In almost 99 per cent of the cases I can think of, the money spent on surgery for purely cosmetic reasons is just as well spent on other things.

I have always been convinced that if only my nose were smaller I would be a ravishing beauty; but I've never had the courage to put my theory to the surgeon's knife. Nothing in life comes free, and you must decide whether you are emotionally ready to trade. To put it bluntly, plastic surgery is a series of exchanges, you get a scar for a wrinkle.

This is not a decision for family and friends. Go to the best doctor and discuss it with him. Most surgeons specialize in one area or another, so make sure you're dealing with the person you need for your particular problem.

One New York specialist I talked to said, 'my patients divide up roughly according to age. The youngest group comes for noses and acne, the oldest group for facelifts. In between are the breasts and bellies.'

If you're young, with a bad feature or unattractive skin, you may want to get them fixed; but it won't bring you success, or money, or Mr Right, unless you have a lot more going for you. If the years have caught up with you, and your face is heavily furrowed, a lift may minimize the wrinkles and make them less apparent, but it will not eliminate them completely. You'll look good, better than you did, but you're not going to get the last twenty years back.

1 Creams can definitely soften wrinkles as they make the skin more supple. They can help plump up some of the lighter, smaller lines; but no cream can completely remove any line or wrinkle.

2 If you have lost a great deal of weight, or had a baby, you may well have stretch marks. Oils, massage and exercise may help avoid these marks in the first place but, once you have them, the only way to remove them is surgery.

3 Varicose veins can easily be removed in a simple stripping operation. To soften the pain until then, wear sheer support hose and get plenty of exercise and walking. Don't ever stand still for prolonged periods.

4 A mild Acid Peel is used to burn off small warts, and is also used for a superficial peel, leaving your skin red and tender. It results in normal looking skin without wrinkles. It clears up bad acne scars, as well as minor surgical scars; and corrects enlarged pores.

5 The Deep Peel is extremely painful, and you may be unable to eat or sleep for a few days. It is done with both acid and taping and causes severe skin blistering. In addition, its main disadvantage is that the new skin is pink like a baby's bottom, and it stops where the acid stopped. Your pigment never comes back, so you must always cover up with foundation.

6 Silicone injections can be used to puff out the skin and minimize wrinkles and sagging skin.

Once a poor job is done, it is much harder to repair it than to start from scratch. If you decide to go ahead, this is not a project to save money on. Your face is the only one you've got, so be prepared to pay for the best.

Facials

I used to be a great fan of facials; it was soothing and relaxing to lie still for an hour and have smooth smelling lotions patted into my face; but after a while I realized that it was making my skin too active and bringing out all the impurities, also known as spots!

Facials also pull and tug at the skin which can't be good, so I vote against them. Sorry Miss Arden!

Sunbathing

Having a tan makes me feel sexy, skinny and healthy. Nothing wrong with any of that if you ask me; but I have been brainwashed enough by all the medical warnings to know that the sun will not only tan my skin, but also destroy the elasticity, so that by my forties I could have very bad wrinkles.

I was born with the type of skin that always goes red before turning brown; but then, during 1976's super sunbathing weather, I started using Clinique's Sun Block, and went brown immediately, no blistering, no peeling.

1 Keep a careful eye on the hours you spend sunbathing, and liberally reapply sun block every time you get out of the water. If you're not swimming, but perspiring heavily, also reapply the cream.

2 The safest way is to start off with two hour-long sessions a day; one between 9 and 11.30 a.m., and the other between 3 and 5 p.m. Be sure to count your time in the water as well as lying in the sun.

3 Take Brewers' Yeast Tablets to increase the B vitamins in your body, which produce the tanning pigment in skin called melanin. The fairer your complexion, the less natural melanin you have.

4 Most fragrances have Oil of Bergamot in them, which, when exposed to the sun, can cause brown splotches to appear on your skin. It's safest to leave off all scent on any exposed part of your body.

5 Caffeine increases sensitivity to the sun, so go easy on coffee, tea, cola drinks and all alcohol.

6 Pay especial attention to thin-skinned areas like feet, ankles, neck, throat, your chest, ears, eyelids, the back of your hands and your lips.

7 Always have a quick shower if you've been in salt water. As it dries, the salt will crust on your skin; it's drying and uncomfortable.

8 When you come in out of the sun, always have a bath or shower, as any type of suntan lotion clogs up your pores.

9 Sand, grass and water, all reflect back the strong ultraviolet rays. So make sure you have plenty of protection, even if you're not deliberately sunbathing.

10 Never use one of those silver paper reflectors. Holding it close to your face rapidly increases the risk of getting a bad sunburn.

11 In the winter, if you use a sun lamp, be very careful. Apply suntan lotion and then sit in front of the lamp. Cover your eyes. Now turn it on; forty-five seconds on the right side of your face, forty-five seconds on the left, one minute facing front. Right, that's it. Don't do it again for twenty-four hours.

12 Use eyedrops after sunbathing to soothe the effects of wind, sun, perspiration and suntan lotion.

13 Ultra-violet rays can filter through clouds and fog, so take the usual precautions on overcast days.

14 Always protect yourself from the effects of snow and sun together.

15 If you suddenly find yourself with the chance to sunbathe, and no protective tanning lotion, a thin layer of your usual foundation will be a sunblock for your face.

16 Choose a suntan lotion that suits you and works, and be generous with it. This is not a situation where less is more.

Don't stop applying it just because you've got your basic coat of tan.

17   The reflection off your sunglasses may keep your nose burnt red. Leave them off for a few days.

18   After sunbathing, cool down your body heat with a tepid bath. Pat yourself dry, and generously apply body lotion while your body is still slightly damp. What your body needs now is moisture. Fluff on talcum powder all over.

19   At the end of the summer, scrub off the last muddy vestiges of your tan by rubbing all over with a Buf-Puf in the bath.

20   It is possible that any medicine you're taking will affect your body's reaction to the sun. Many women I know who are on the pill say that they've developed brown spots on their faces and chests when exposed to the sun; the pill may be a catalyst for them. Brown, so-called liver, spots, especially on the back of your hands, may get darker.

21   If you have had too much sun, and your skin feels very sensitive, soak in a bath with one-third of a cup of baking soda stirred in. After you've patted yourself dry, apply Calamine Lotion to the red areas.

22   If your face gets burnt, strong tea will take away the sting. Brew up a cup with tea bags and when they are cool, pat them on your face. Lie down until the tannic acid dries; then rinse your face with cool water.

23   If your eyes are bloodshot and puffy, soak two cotton handkerchiefs in ice water. Wring them out and place them on your closed eyes. Lie down for ten minutes and relax.

24   Half our total weight is liquid, and during hot weather we lose more than normal through perspiration. I swear by lots of soda water with a teaspoon of fresh lemon juice. Cool and no calories.

25   Lucinda taught me a trick last year when she came back from Christmas skiing and wanted to keep her healthy tan look. She used a little Guerlain Teint Doré as foundation. I, for one, couldn't tell it wasn't real.

Facial Hair

This is a problem that most women are embarrassed to talk about. It ranges from a soft overall down to strong dark hairs on the chin, upper lip, around the eyebrows and in front of the ears.

1   One of the highest paid models in New York, who is the 'face' for a grand cosmetic company, told me years ago that she shaved her face with an electric razor, because otherwise the facial hair made her foundation look streaky. The alternative for complete removal is a cream depilatory, but it is possible you'll get a rash from the chemicals.

2   If you have a light fuzz, but the hairs are a little dark, you can bleach the hairs. Nestle Lite Hair Lightener is perfect for this. You'll probably have to redo it every two or three weeks.

3   Electrolysis is the only permanent hair removal. I've had it done on my upper lip and to clear out some of the stragglers under my eyebrows. It wasn't particularly painful, and I hate hairy faces, so I think it's a worthwhile investment. If you're very sensitive, hold ice cubes against the skin so it's slightly numb before you start.

You may need anything from six to two dozen treatments before the hair is completely eradicated. Choose a competent, trained operator, and she'll be able to give you some idea before you begin. I find that after only two or three treatments the hair is noticeably weaker.

4   An alternative method is called Depilex, but I've been told it doesn't work nearly as well as electrolysis. An electrical current is supposed to travel down the hair shaft, but it's so weak it takes a great deal longer to kill the hair.

5   If the down on your face is noticeable, you can have it waxed. Even if it's the fairest shade of blond, it gets reflected in the light. One quick pull and the worst is over. I won't attempt any home waxing; it's a lot tougher to do yourself, and the cost of replacing a ruined carpet will pay for a considerable number of salon treatments.

A tip to soften the pang of pain in waxing. Press your hand hard, on the spot, the moment the wax has been pulled off. I don't know why, but the sting disappears immediately.

6 If your hairline is badly shaped, or if you'd like to create a widow's peak, get rid of heavy sideburns, or just generally change it, the only lasting way to do it is electrolysis.

Medicine

At some time or another in our lives, all of us take medicine and suffer no disastrous side-effects. Pain can be intolerable, but quickly cured; or it can be advance warning of something serious. I'm a great believer that, if anything goes on hurting, you should go to a doctor, quick.

1 Stress affects all of us, and there are times when the occasional tranquilliser helps us make it through the day. If they're a habit, and you'll know, get off them now. I got horrible migraines when I was working at the *Sunday Times*, and the only way I could stop them was with massive doses of aspirin and Valium. Even though I rarely talked about it, a boyfriend told me that he could always tell when I'd had an attack, because the effect of all those drugs showed in my eyes for days. I don't know what he saw, but he scared the living daylights out of me, and I cut back pretty sharp.

2 Sleeping pills may work when you first start taking them, but after a week or two they are less effective, even in increased dosages. See the Sleep section below, and find a more healthy system to help you get a good night's rest.

3 Diet pills are usually based on amphetamines – speed or uppers in the parlance – and are almost always addictive. You quickly build up a resistance to them, and you'll find yourself hooked even though they're no longer helping you to lose weight. They are dangerous, and it's just not worth it.

4 Diuretics are also supposed to make you lose weight because they make your kidneys work overtime, and clear your body of liquids. Very few of us have a serious problem of retaining fluids, and the effect of a diuretic is very temporary. Within two or three days your natural thirst will have rebalanced itself and your body will be back to being half fluid.

Most doctors I've talked to are very wary of prescribing diuretics, and they're not available without a prescription for good reason.

5   Birth control methods. Today there are so many alternatives that at least one should suit your body. All have disadvantages as well as advantages; only you can make the best
choice. Birth control pills are under constant review and dis-
cussion, and any doubts or fears you have should be instantly
discussed with your doctor.

6   I've never been pregnant, so I've never been faced with
the moral decision of whether I should take medicine or not
during these nine months. But the more I read and hear, the
more I think that if I were responsible for the potential well-
being of another human being, I would do everything possible to bear any pain or discomfort without medicine. Doctors now know that drugs pass directly from mother to the
unborn baby; that's a monumental responsibility to take
chances with.

   I've taken pain killers when I've had to. I'm not enough of
a martyr, and too much of a coward, not to, but, long-term, I
think overuse of drugs shows up in how you look, and it's a
minus, not a plus.

After living in England for four years I developed hayfever which
made the summers a misery for me. Last year I started a course of
injections and found I was almost completely cured. Anyone with
any allergy should hie themselves to an allergist. Allergies are
almost all controllable.

Alcohol

I loathe the taste and smell of alcohol, and I can't imagine why
anyone would rather drink spirits than Coca-Cola. Although I do
see the pleasure in a glass of Château-Lafite, it is a decidedly
expensive taste to acquire. And even though my usual tipple of
Perrier water can get pretty boring, spiced up with lots of ice
cubes, and a slice of lemon, it has got no calories and no disastrous
side-effects.

   Only you can decide the amount of pleasure alcohol gives you,
and whether it outweighs the disadvantages. I'd much rather eat
the calories!

   1   If you're having spirits, have them straight. Tonic water
   or ginger ale add lots of calories.

2 Heavy drinkers don't eat properly because alcohol sends excessive amounts of sugar into the bloodstream and causes loss of appetite.

3 Spirits devour Vitamin B, and break down protein, which leaves you feeling weak and listless.

4 Heavy drinkers get blotched and pasty skin, and puffy eyes.

5 Alcohol is bad for your skin because both spirits and wine are very acid.

6 If you do drink, always have a tablespoon of pure lemon juice in a cup of hot water first thing in the morning to break down the acid. Also drink at least six glasses of water during the day.

7 Has your complexion got an olive tinge to it? Give up all spirits for two weeks and see if your skin looks pinker and clearer. That drab hue may come straight out of a bottle.

Drink offers many pleasures: it may relax you; send you flying; compensate for disappointments and unhappiness; and, taken in moderation, you're unlikely to end up with the DTs, but more than that, and you'll add years to your skin. Is it worth it?

Smoking

Sorry about this, but I can't discover one thing to say in favour of smoking. It damages your lungs, heart, skin, eyes, fingernails and hair. It gives you discoloured teeth, smelly hands and hair, clogged pores, premature wrinkles, smoker's breath, bad circulation and nicotine yellow skin.

Smoking is even bad for sex. The Americans have produced a study, according to *Vogue*, showing that menopause occurs several years earlier among smokers, suggesting that smoking affects the sexual hormones.

Cigarettes consume your body's supply of Vitamin C, and destroy lecithin which is what breaks down fats and keeps them from being deposited in the arteries as cholesterol. Inhaling sends carbon monoxide into the blood and destroys oxygen in the red blood cells. If you smoke a pack a day, you'll reduce the flow of oxygen to your heart and lungs by 15 per cent, and it takes four to six hours to expel that carbon monoxide from your body.

And now for the good news! As soon as you give up smoking, or at least radically cut down on your intake, your complexion will start to clear up, and your eyes will start getting brighter again. Isn't it worth it? If by any remote chance you're still going to smoke, then please, never while walking in the street. And no one should ever chew gum in the street either.

Sleep

'A good night's sleep' sounds like a cliché, but it's still a worthwhile beauty recipe. Only you know how much your own body needs, and it is certainly true that we need less sleep as we get older. Ten years ago I was in no fit state for anything without at least ten hours every night; now I'm raring to go with seven or eight.

Make sure you get as much as you need. Tiredness makes us bad-tempered, jittery and prone to pick up any bug going around. You may also think it puts those dark circles under your eyes, but in fact, dark pigment is there to reduce glare, and nature may just have given you more, rather than less.

Insomnia can suddenly strike anyone, of any age, with no advance warning. Doctors can offer no infallible cure and there's no magic formula to avoid becoming an insomniac in the first place.

It may stem from poor health, depression, old age or anxieties about things that in the light of day seem trivial. Insomnia often compounds itself: lose sleep one night over a problem, and the next night you may toss and turn, because you're so worried about last night's sleeplessness.

Experts do make certain suggestions, though, so see if any of these help you.

1 Establish a routine by going to bed every night at the same time. Your body will get used to the regular pattern and fall asleep out of habit.
2 In the hour before bedtime, relax both your muscles and your nerves. Do five minutes of deep yoga breathing. Inhale deeply and expand your stomach so that it pushes hard against your hands. Hold for a count of two, and then blow

out through your mouth until your stomach flattens under your hands. Don't be surprised if you start yawning. Follow this with a hot bath, and instead of harsh electric lights, bathe by candlelight while you listen to soft music on your transistor; never fool with electrical objects while you're wet. Blood heat is the most soothing of all temperatures. After a few minutes, run the hot tap until you feel as if you've been in a sauna, then step out, blot yourself dry, soothe on body lotion and slide into bed.

3 Don't read a frightening mystery or watch a violent TV show; both of which will accelerate your pulse rate.

4 Avoid coffee, tea, Coca-Cola and cigarettes: all of which are stimulants. Don't eat a heavy meal or any highly spiced food just before going to bed. If you're hungry, have some yoghurt. A glass of hot milk, which contains the sleep inducing trytophan amino acid may help. Calcium is a natural tranquillizer, so if you prefer, take three calcium lactate tablets with a hot herbal tea like camomile, skullcap, catnip, peppermint, vervain or passaflora.

5 Drinking large quantities of spirits produces fragmented sleep, and often leads to nightmares. A single glass of wine or beer, however, may help.

6 Make your bedroom as comfortable as possible. Experiment with different depths of darkness until you find what suits you best. Also decide how much fresh air you like. Avoid having the room too hot and dry, as dryness can parch your throat and keep you awake. Consider the use of a room humidifier if necessary.

7 A solid mattress, not necessarily rock hard, is essential. If yours is soft and lumpy, and you can't afford a new one right away, put a bedboard, even an old door, underneath it until you have the money. Too hard a mattress will find you waking with aches and pains.

8 Men find sex a very effective soporific. It has been sending them to sleep for centuries. Women usually stay awake after making love, so allow for it.

9 Try repetitive mind games such as counting sheep, or backwards from 100.

10 Don't become dependent on sleeping pills. Using them

regularly often produces side-effects and lessens their effectiveness. Large doses, combined with alcohol, can be fatal.

11 Don't take long naps in the afternoon, or the early evening, while you are establishing a set sleep pattern. Force yourself to stay awake until the bedtime you have set.

12 If you fall asleep for three or four hours, and then awaken, don't lie there worrying about it. Get up, have a warm drink, read or listen to music.

Finally, if you do lose a night's sleep, don't worry – you can always catch up tomorrow.

Manicures

I didn't consider hands an erogenous zone until I sat next to William at lunch one day. He's a devotee of feminine charms, and I noticed that as he commented on the women going to and fro in the restaurant, he was noting their hands nearly as quickly as their faces. When I asked, he said that bad hands turned him off a great deal faster than ugliness; which made me take a hard look at my own hands.

As a child, I used to bite my nails so badly that I permanently walked around with my fingers bent into my palms, trying to hide the evidence of the dreaded habit. I tried every trick in the book to stop: foul tasting liquids painted on; band aids glued across the tips; cotton gloves worn everywhere except the bath. Nothing helped, I was an addicted nail biter.

I was about sixteen when I stopped, for no apparent reason. But even though they grew long, and I spent time polishing them and keeping them well shaped, they often split and broke, and didn't seem strong enough to stand up to an ordinary day's wear and tear. Having read endless advertising claims for nail cure products, I finally decided to test them out. Now, the hours spent on treating them has certainly paid off, and they're both long and hard.

I set up my kit in my dressing-table drawer, so that everything is all together when I've got the ten minutes it takes me to look after them.

No matter how careful I am, I find I have to replace polish every three or four days. It naturally chips, and covering up the damage makes the entire nail surface peel, so it's better to start at the beginning again.

Supplies

Nail polish remover
Cotton wool
Mavala Super Base Protector
Revlon and Estée Lauder Coloured varnishes
Emery boards
Small sharp nail scissors
Revlon Cuticle Remover
Mavala Scientific Nail Hardener
Mavala Mavaderma
Orange stick
Hand cream
Nail file

1   Twice a week, begin by removing all the old varnish: soak a piece of cotton wool with varnish remover and hold it against the nail for a few seconds. Stroke cotton to the end of the nail, but don't rub, or the old enamel will be reapplied to the nail. Wash your hands to make sure all the remover is gone, as it can be very drying to the skin.

2   File any nail that needs it; use the fine side of the emery board, moving it from the side of the nail to the centre. Never saw back and forth to a point, or deep into the corner. As the nails begin to grow, keep the sides straight, and the tips blunt, so that they are less likely to snag on things and break.

3   Soak hands in warm soapy water to soften the cuticles. After drying, use cuticle remover. Massage gently into the cuticles and push back with the blunt end of a nail file, working away the dead tissue. Rinse well. Never cut your cuticles, it's the worst thing in the world for them and, by using the cuticle remover cream, they stay soft and supple, and don't get jagged and messy looking. If you push the cuticles back too hard, you may eventually find yourself with ridges on the nail surface as it grows out during the next few months.

4   Paint on Mavala Scientific Nail Hardener, a thin green

liquid. Only put it on the white part of your nail because it really does make them hard, and if the nail breaks, you don't want it to be below the tip of your finger. For the first month, use it twice a week when you put on new varnish. When the nails are long and hard, use it only twice a month.

5   Next comes a coat of Mavala Super Base Protector, which fills in ridges and irregularities, creating a smooth surface. The formula contains acrylic and protein to help toughen them and, just as important, prevents the next coat of coloured varnish from staining the nail.

6   Then use two coats of enamel, making sure the first is dry before you apply the second. I choose the darkest red colours as I find them a great boost to my self-control. Every chip shows, so that I'm constantly reminded to stop chewing on them. I always pick flat 'creme' colours as they look far more expensive and high fashion than the frosteds, which were big in the sixties.

7   For every coat on top, also put one under the tip. It gives them that much extra protection. I don't bother with a special top coat as it is an extra expense, and when I tested one I didn't find the varnish lasted any longer.

8   In the winter I like a very deep dark Burgundy colour as it balances heavier, more sombre clothes, and it also makes my hands look whiter and more delicate. In the summer, when I'm tanned, a pale pink looks pretty, and shows off the colour of my skin.

9   It's very rare that all my nails are equally long. Even though the experts say to file the longer ones down to match any that are broken, I can't bear to do it, so they are different lengths; but who cares?

10   All the cosmetic companies offer a large selection of nail enamel colours, and other companies such as Sally Hansen and Nailoid specialize in treatment products. With such a vast choice, look around and decide what suits you. For instance, there are various nail-shaped transparent films to protect a broken nail, but I just picked them off, so for me they're a waste of money.

11   Stay away from the fake nails that are a powder and liquid mix like dental fillings. When it dries, it becomes as

hard as cement, and Julie lost almost all her nails after using them. I tried those ready-shaped plastic ones that models often use for photography, but they just snapped off.

12 Revlon produce a solvent to thin down nail enamels which infuriatingly thicken before you've been able to use half the bottle.

13 Every night, before going to bed, massage Mavala's Mavaderma into each finger just below the crescent of the nail. It is a nourishing product which enters the root and hardens the nail even before it emerges to the surface.

I know that addicted nail biters think they'll never be able to stop, but with will power you can, and the pleasure and pride you'll feel is immense. I'm so proud of my nails now that I almost want to carry around a 'before' picture, so that people can tell what a difference there is. Chewed-off nails aren't just a big turn-off, they are also a pretty good give-away to exactly how insecure and unsure of yourself you are. If, like me, you use your hands a lot when you're talking, don't you have a responsibility to your audience to make them look nice?

Here are some protective nail tips:

1 Wear rubber gloves when doing the dishes or cleaning the house. Water is the worst thing for your hands and nails, because it dries out your skin, and weakens the nails.

2 Always wear gloves when you're gardening, as finger infections are quite common to gardeners. Another safeguard is to squash lots of softened soap under your fingernails. This acts as a barrier to earth getting ground in.

3 If you want gardening, or rubber, gloves also to work as a beauty aid, put on a thick slather of handcream before you pull them on.

4 As your nails start growing long, automatically pick up small objects by sliding them to the edge of the surface, so that you can lift them with your finger tips.

5 Use the rubber end of a pencil to dial the telephone.

6 Push back the cuticles with a towel after you've washed your hands, and always use handcream after they've been in water.

7   After a manicure, keep your hands out of water for as many hours as possible so that the enamel has completely hardened.

Pedicures

It makes me feel very sexy to stick red toenails out from under the bedcovers, and I give myself a pedicure every two weeks. Toenails appear to grow more slowly than fingernails, and there's not as much wear and tear to damage the varnish.

1   Remove the old enamel with cotton wool saturated with varnish remover.
2   File the nails straight across, and never into the corners, or they'll get ingrown.
3   Use cuticle remover cream, and then soak your feet in hot sudsy water for five minutes. Pumice the calloused or rough areas on the soles of your feet, the heels and the toes. Scholls do a fabulous steel callous remover, on a handle, which is better than any pumice stone. Never use a razor blade to remove the dead skin.

Callous remover

4   Dry your feet well, and then apply a coat of colourless polish before two coats of coloured varnish. If you find it difficult to separate the toes, twist a couple of tissues between each toe.
5   Rub body lotion into the feet.

You may experience discomfort from corns: either hard ones on the joint of the little toe, or soft ones between the toes. Both are caused by friction and pressure from shoes. They can be removed by a chiropodist, but I have one on my left little toe that always comes back anyway, so if they're not painful, or too unsightly, just leave them.

Spectacles

Obviously, the only reason for wearing glasses is defective eyesight. Eye strain gives you headaches; makes you wrinkle your brow; or the light bothers you so that you squint. Smoke, tiredness or bad lighting may leave your eyes bloodshot. Only a professional ophthalmologist can tell you if you need glasses and, if you're suffering from any suspicious symptoms, please go and see him.

There are no firm and fast rules for how far away to hold your book, or how close to sit to the telly. 'A comfortable distance' was the professional answer when I asked. Proper light does have a lot to do with eye comfort; the smaller the type, the brighter the light is always a safe rule.

Avoid glare, you don't want to see the bulb that's lighting your work. And don't let the light bounce back into your eyes.

If you have to wear glasses on medical grounds, and agree with Dorothy Parker that 'Men seldom make passes at girls who wear glasses', consider contact lenses. Ten years ago, millions of potential users found them so uncomfortable they had to give up, but all sorts of new types are now available, and you should be able to find one that suits you. Talk to your eye specialist and see what he says.

The fact that you wear glasses has nothing to do with the hair style you choose. Your glasses should have an aesthetic shape that suits you. Stay away from garish designs and glitter colours: the classic tortoiseshell is still the most attractive. You don't want people to see the glasses, and then you. You want them to see you, wearing glasses.

Accentuate your eye make-up behind glasses. Emphasize your eyes so that they hold their own against the frames: highlight the browbone, accentuate the eyelid socket, use lots and lots of mascara. If you wear false eyelashes, be sure you have them on when you are being fitted for glasses, otherwise your lashes may hit the lenses.

Sunglasses are worn not only by people with eye problems, but as a fashion accessory. Driving, or outdoors, in a climate like England's, you need a glass that filters out 70 per cent of the light. On the beach, or wherever there's a strong glare, you want between 75 and 85 per cent of the light filtered. Any good lens is going to block out the ultra-violet rays along with the light. Look for ground glass lenses, which are worth the extra cost. The newest lenses are sun sensitive, but with any others, use this test. Try glasses on in front of a mirror, stand back; if you can see your eyes clearly, they're not dark enough. Again, I think the frames should be tortoiseshell, or at least dark. No whites, no pales, no glitter.

Lots of women like using sunglasses as a headband. It started with socialites and movie starlets in the swinging sixties; back when we all had great manes of teased out hair. For some reason it annoys men; ignore their jibes, and go right on doing it.

Teeth

I can't even count all the people I know whose good looks are ruined when they open their mouths. Is it because their teeth are inside that they never realize how noticeable they are? Every time you speak, or smile, they show, so they had better be good, and the sooner you do something about them the better.

If teeth are nearly rotted away, they can be replaced with dentures and bridge work, but most dentists think that, properly cared for, teeth should last your lifetime.

Generally speaking, good adult teeth mean that they were properly looked after when you were a child, but up to about the age of thirty, crooked or protruding teeth can still be improved by orthodontia, but it is an expensive process, and takes longer than when you're young. If you inherited teeth that have a yellowish tinge to them, there is no cream or polish on the market that can turn them white for you. If the colour is so bad that it's ruining your looks, the only solution is to have the teeth crowned, but that is a very drastic, and expensive, solution.

Until the age of twenty-five, a tooth may have to be taken out because the crown, meaning the white visible part, is decayed. After twenty-five, it's peridontal disease: disease of the gums and roots of the teeth, that causes them to die. At any age, what destroys teeth is the combination of sugar with dental plaque, a nasty substance made of millions of bacteria which coat your teeth.

No matter how carefully you brush your teeth, 10 per cent of the plaque remains, and sugar combining with the plaque produces lactic acid and dissolves the enamel. How much sugar you eat is unimportant; what counts is the number of times you eat it, because each time the sugar sparks off twenty minutes of acid production.

To find out how much plaque there is on your teeth, buy some disclosing tablets at your local chemist. Brush your teeth as usual, and chew one of the tablets. It contains a harmless vegetable dye which will stain any remaining plaque. The most likely places are where teeth meet each other, or the line where the tooth goes into the gums. Brush them again, and when there is no trace of dye left, you'll know they're perfectly clean.

After a few days' practice, you'll redevelop your tooth brushing technique so as to remove all the plaque first go. I eventually found that in order to get them perfectly clean, I had to use dental floss as well, which is also easily obtainable at the chemist's. After brushing, snap off a 10-inch length and wind it around your two index fingers. Slide it between all your teeth, working from left to right, using a slight sawing motion.

It doesn't matter what sort of toothbrush you use, as long as it does the job properly; and toothpaste makes your mouth taste good, and stops halitosis, but it really has very little to do with cleaning.

During a cold, or if you have a bug or some form of low grade fever, you may get some slight bleeding of the gums. At any other time, this is a sign that there is something amiss with your system. If it lasts for more than a few days, do go and see your dentist, with whom you must have a yearly check-up anyway. That visit is a necessity. I would hate to lose the gamble, and find myself with a mouthful of false teeth at the age of fifty.

Photographs

At some point, all of us have to have our picture taken. Some women always look good; others come out badly, yet in real life they're every bit as attractive as the camera beauty. Put simply, the photogenic face has wide-set eyes, small features, good cheek-bones and a firm jawline.

However, since we would all like to be photogenic, and there are times when we must be, it is worthwhile to get it right. Certain angles of any face look better than others, and so it's useful to get your face photographed from every side, so that you can figure out which is the best one. Years ago, Patrick Lichfield was photographing me, and after just a few seconds of looking through the lens, he commented on something I'd only been vaguely aware of: that the two sides of my face are very different, and my long beak has a more sharply defined shape from the left; which makes the entire face much more photogenic from an angle to the left, with the nose slightly turned away. Now, when a camera hoves into view I automatically turn my face at the right angle, and leave the rest to the gods.

Analysing photographs, even the bad ones, can often teach you about your own features. Once you've seen your face as the camera does, choose the best available photographer and relax.

Forget about the camera, and pretend it's not there. If the idea of facing the camera makes you shake with fear, take a tranquil-lizer. Or, instead of a pill, have a small drink. I also think music makes a big difference, and takes you outside yourself.

A photographer is a professional: he'll do his best to put you at your ease. If, for any reason, you don't like him, you're going to fight subconsciously, and it will show in the pictures. Find some-one else, and don't waste time.

I happen to be a ham through and through, so having my pic-ture taken is a natural high. Try flirting with the camera; it will show in your eyes, and light up the photograph.

8 ❧ Looking After Your Hair

Choosing your Hairdresser

The biggest moral support in your life is going to be your hairdresser, so choose him – or her – with as much passion and care as you do your husband. Even if you only go to him for a trim every six weeks, he has an all-important influence on your looks.

You may have a dozen false starts before you finally find someone on the same wavelength as you. Once you've found him, stick to him through thick and thin, or else you'll be just another head to cut and set. Liking is going to be nearly as important as talent because, if you grate on each other's nerves, your hair will suffer.

The first time someone new does your hair, he won't, and you won't, want to make any radical change. It will take him at least that one session to understand the growth pattern and texture of your hair. Once you've become a steady client, I don't think it's presumptuous to assume that if there's an emergency, and you walk in desperate, he'll squeeze you in somehow.

No one knows more about my hair than I do; after all, I've had to live with it, but I can share that knowledge with my hairdresser, which will make his life, as well as mine, a lot simpler.

Helping your Hairdresser

1 Tell him your life style.
2 How your man likes, and doesn't like, you to look.
3 Show him any hair pictures you've liked and cut out.

4 Be sure and tell him when you're pleased with what he's done.

5 Be flexible and let him try new styles.

6 Don't be too embarrassed, if you're not pleased with his work, to switch to someone else in the same salon.

7 Don't expect him to do the same thing for you he does for your friend. You might look less alike than you think.

8 Be realistic: a new hair-do alone won't remake your looks.

9 Tell him how much time you're willing, or able, to spend on your hair every day.

10 How good are you with your hands? Can you learn?

11 What do you like about your looks, or dislike, the most?

12 What do you want out of a style, how long must the set last?

All the big salons have teaching sessions for their juniors a couple of nights a week. For only a fraction of the regular price, you can be cut and styled under the close supervision of a senior member of the staff. A bargain opportunity to try one of the high fashion salons, and guaranteed safe. In the same vein, the Vidal Sassoon School is always looking for creative models.

I've been thoroughly spoilt because, through my job, three of the best hairdressers in the world have done my hair. *Glamour* sent me to Kenneth, when he wasn't busy doing Jackie Kennedy's famous bouffant, to restyle my hair. The result was pretty, but not spectacular, and I wasn't objective enough to see what his subtle change had done to soften and frame my face. I'm now ashamed to say that after the photography was finished, I went back to my much more severe style.

Later Leonard cut my ribcage length hair into a minuscule bob which changed the way I walked and dressed and thought about myself. Formerly, I'd always looked for 'pretty' clothes, but now sportswear began to look more appropriate for this tomboy hair-cut.

Then Clifford Stafford took over my head, and since then it has been, 'we're going to cut it short'; or, 'now we feel like wearing it longer'. Sometimes it's 'this month we feel like ringlets', or, 'while we're growing it out, let's try a perm'. It makes me laugh when he talks about what 'we're' going to do, but that's exactly the sort of relationship I think every woman should have with her 'crimper', as Vidal Sassoon likes to call his trade.

Clifford knows I wash my hair every day; that any setting is wasted; that I hate sticky lotions and hair spray; don't have the patience to sit under a drier; and that what I want is soft, shiny hair that is smooth to the touch and easy to look after.

Although he had already stopped styling hair himself by the time we became friends some five years ago, Vidal Sassoon is not only an astonishing talent but one of the nicest celebrities I've ever encountered, and the least phony or affected by his world-wide fame. 'My job,' he said, 'was to make women look beautiful,' and today his salons, spread across the world, do just that.

Hair Care

The way your hair looks tells as much about you as wearing a bill board. If you're healthy, your hair will be shiny and glossy, as thick at the ends as it is at the roots. If you're nervous and unhappy, your scalp will tighten up, and your hair will look lifeless from lack of circulation. If you don't look after your hair with regular haircuts, you're going to have split ends.

Healthy hair is not just a frame for your face, but a sensual living part of people's reaction to you. If your hair isn't sexy and strokable, you're making a mistake somewhere.

1 Never, in any circumstances, be seen in public with your hair in rollers.
2 If you suffer from oily hair, keep to a low fat diet, don't wash it with too hot water and, in between, apply astringent on a wad of cotton wool to your scalp.
3 If you have very oily hair, keep it back with a headband when you sleep, so that the oil doesn't cause spots on your face.
4 Hair spray doesn't do much for any type of hair, so use as little as possible. Use a spray which has a very fine mist and spray from about 6 to 7 inches away.
5 Never use heated rollers when your hair is damp, only when it is dry.
6 Use left-over flat beer as a setting lotion. Pour it into a

plastic mist-spray bottle and lightly spray it on to your damp hair. The smell quickly disappears, but it gives the hair bounce and body.

7 If you need to use heated rollers every day; wrap a piece of Kleenex or very thin foam rubber around them so that your hair is protected from the spikes of the roller. It is impossible to pull a spiked roller out of your hair; instead, gently unwind it.

8 Never use hair pins or clips unless they have plastic-coated tips.

9 Don't dry your hair in front of any type of fire; direct heat will not only dry it out, it may scorch it.

10 If you continuously pull your hair back very tightly, it may cause breakage about $\frac{1}{2}$ inch from the root.

11 There's only one permanent cure for split ends; cut them off.

12 If you use setting lotion on very fine hair, towel dry it first to mop up excess moisture before applying the lotion.

13 Any hormone change in your body may cause your hair to fall out. Pregnancy, going off the pill, menopause, all may cause temporary problems, but eventually your body will readjust itself.

14 To cope with static electricity, most good conditioners contain an anti-static ingredient.

15 If you swim in either salt or chlorinated water, be sure to rinse with fresh water before it dries on your hair.

16 If you don't eat a balanced diet, your hair will show it. Hair is 97 per cent protein, so be sure your body gets enough fish, poultry, meat and dairy products, as well as fresh fruit and vegetables. Vitamin B is also a great help, but sleeping pills have a noticeably negative effect.

17 Normal heads lose about a hundred hairs a day; not enough for the eye to notice. Poor diet, tension, bad circulation, or too many cigarettes and spirits can increase this loss radically.

18 Long hair doesn't split any faster than short, it just looks that way because it's not cut as often.

19 The bigger a roller you use, the looser the curl. If you use a skinny roller, you'll end up with a tight curl.

20 If you have to tease your hair for more body, use a large comb with wide-apart teeth, never a brush or a teasing comb.
21 Hair texture is inherited, and average growth is about half an inch a month, or slightly more in a hot climate.

Quite honestly, I can't understand any woman who has her hair done every week in a hair salon, and can't look after it herself. If you're pressed for cash, think how much you must be doing without in order to get your hair set. You must be spending £5 a week on it, £20 a month, £240 a year; which would buy a large number of clothes.

Hair Cuts

A good cut makes your hair look good even when it's at its worst; but a bad cut can't be turned into a good hair-do by any power on earth. Damaged hair can only be cured by cutting.

Fine hair gets pulled down by its weight if it's left long. Cut it as short as looks good, and you'll find it has more body. It takes three or four days after a cut for the hair to settle naturally into place. Don't judge any haircut too quickly. I always hate mine at first then, suddenly, it's all right and I love it.

If you need a hair-style to last, sleep on a slippery satin pillow case. There's no friction against your hair so the set stays in place.

A vast quantity of hair, teased and combed, compensates for insignificant features. But most women today have simplified their hair-styles. The hair is either very short, impeccably cut; or grown shoulder length and worn nearly straight and swinging.

There used to be a hard and fast rule that as you got older your hair had to get shorter; in fact, what hairdressers were trying to achieve was an optical illusion that the face lines were 'lifted'. Long hair, hanging down, draws attention, even if subliminally, to drooping lines and sagging flesh. It's not the hair length that's so important, but the lines and angles it emphasizes, and a softer wave to the hair will soften the face as well.

It's obvious that long hair offers more variety of styles than short, and although there is more of it, it is often easier to maintain as well. Men are still suckers, even in this liberated age, for girls wearing their hair up. Maybe it's the thought that it might come down; with a fantasy of hairpins slipping out through his fingers.

The hazard of short hair is not the daily regime which, even if you wash it every day as I do, still amounts to only minutes; but the shape is so all-important that I find it needs to be trimmed after two weeks, and has outgrown the shape after three.

The most extraordinary thing about a haircut is that it can change your looks so radically that your personality alters to suit it as well. Even more disconcerting, people don't recognize me if I've cut my hair short since the last time they saw me. I'm still walking around behind the same face, so it's all very difficult to understand.

A hairdresser today creates a hair-style that works for your face, your shape and your size. If you have to force your hair into a style with either a heavy setting lotion or a great deal of lacquer, something is wrong, and your hair isn't naturally happy with the cut or the shape. If you're given a cut that you don't like you must say so, while you're still in the chair. In most cases it can be altered, but it may also be a question of getting used to it, so tell your stylist you doubt whether it's right for you, but that you'd like to test it.

Keep in mind that no hair-do is going to look fabulous if your face is much fatter than it ought to be. If you're having your hair cut at the start of an ambitious diet, confide in the hairdresser, as he will probably want to take that into account as he works.

The only way to learn how to do fantastic tricks with your hair is to watch, and then practise. Look at all the new magazines while you're waiting, or under the drier, but keep your eye peeled for what's happening while there's any action going on. If you can tell the effect he's getting, but not how he's doing it, ask, he'll be flattered.

For a year, Clifford cut my hair with a parting on the right side, and brushed the fringe from right to left. For a year, I thanked him profusely, went home, washed it, parted it on the left and swept the fringe from left to right. I finally got around to mentioning this to Clifford, who, after giving me a disgusted look, quietly pointed out that by combing my fringe, which covers three cowlicks, against the hair growth, it looks twice as thick. Now I do it his way, and I'm only sorry I was too stupid to ask why last year.

132

The same advice goes for a blow-dry that depends on a hand drier and a brush; or putting in rollers; or twisting a chignon. Watch, and copy. It's free.

One thing I have learned from years of working on photographic sittings is that most hair-dos you see in pictures collapse the moment the camera goes click; or else are so lacquered that if your head dissolved, the hair would still stand at attention.

To do a hair story for the *Daily Express* last summer, my hair was completely set three times between 10 and 11.30 a.m.; all for a pensive picture with lots of soft curls. So, do understand all the drawbacks to wanting to look like the photographs.

There are two things to avoid:

1 Never go to a stylist who cuts with a razor instead of scissors. Thinning out your hair will be disastrous, not just the way it looks, but long-term, as it grows in. Whatever style you're having, hair should be blunt cut.

2 A really good hairdresser always cuts hair wet. He'll check it for the final touches when it's dry; but wet is right.

How to Cut your own Hair

For a multitude of reasons, there may come a day when you have to cut your hair yourself. Herewith a simple step-by-step guide, but before you begin, some helpful hints.

The safest length, and the most flexible, is just above the shoulders, blunt cut.

Always leave hair a little longer than you want. Remember, you're cutting wet hair which will be slightly shorter when dry. If your hair is curly, don't cut it too short. It should be short enough to curl by itself, and long enough to frame your face.

Before you begin: have the necessary supplies at hand. A pair of four-inch scissors which you use only on your hair. A full-length mirror, which is well lit. A wide-toothed comb, and a good hair brush. A second mirror which can be moved around.

Get in a good mood. Relax and be patient. Cutting hair is a tedious process, and you can't afford to rush it.

1 Wash and condition your hair.

2 Comb through wet hair: make a centre parting down to the nape of your neck, and separate hair into four sections, by

bisecting the parting from ear to ear. Pin three sections up out of the way. Loose section will be cut in several steps by sub-sectioning into half a dozen horizontal layers.

3 Separate out the bottom sub-section, and pin up the rest. Use this section as your guiding length, and measure all the rest by it. Choose the length you want and leave a little extra. Cut.

4 Unpin the next section, and comb it over the 'guide' section. Trim flush. Continue until all hair in quadrant is cut. Repeat on the other side. Leave the first side hanging free so that you can make sure they are even.

5 The same method is used on the two back sections, but they are a bit trickier. Position one mirror in front, and another behind, so that you are able to see what you are doing.

6 Cut fringe a little long, as it'll be shorter when dry. Use your eyebrows as a guideline. Part in centre and clip fringe to either side. Section off the small middle strand, and then trim the other sections to match it. Cut them slightly jagged, so they look natural.

Haircut

Straightening

In the swinging sixties, it was fashionable to have long flowing bobs, and if you were unlucky enough not to look like Alice In Wonderland, straightening was the only answer. In fact, straightening is the worst possible thing you can do to your hair.

It's really a permanent wave in reverse; no curling rods are used, but the chemical solution is applied, and the hair combed straight. Whatever your hair texture, the hardest section to do is around the nape of the neck, and the hairline at the temples.

Hair that has been straightened is weak; and needs protection from the sun and salt water, the same as coloured or permed hair. Worst of all, the hair is left looking dry and lifeless. It's a silly, and sometimes dangerous, waste of money. Much better to have it cut all one length, which will make it look straighter.

Anne is a fellow New Yorker who came to live in London when she married an Englishman. She has fabulous long, dark, heavy hair that I always assumed was bone straight, until I bumped into her at Leonard's, and discovered how it's done.

Wash your hair, comb smooth and gently towel it dry. Then put two hair clips criss-crossing each other on your crown. Wrap all your hair around your head, going in one direction. Put in hair clips to hold it in place and let dry for about half an hour. Take out the clips, and comb it around your head going in the opposite direction. Clip it down until the hair is completely dry. Then take out the hair clips and lightly brush.

If you're especially dextrous, you can also try this trick: wrap one section of hair at a time around the bristle part of a rounded-head hairbrush; aim the hot air from a small hand drier at the clump of hair, and pull gently on the brush until the hair pulls free, and the kink is gone.

Permanent Waves

Any chemical you use on your hair, however carefully it is applied, is going to affect its condition, so after years of suffering over the inadequacy of my baby-fine, bone-straight hair, I am finally convinced that the most sensible course of action is to get a haircut that makes the most of what nature gave you, and leave it at that.

But, if you don't agree with me, it's reassuring to know that eventually any damaged hair grows out, and you get a second chance. However, please do me one favour: never give yourself a home perm. I know the box top says they are gentle enough for anyone to use, but how gentle can anything really be if it makes your hair curl and, anyway, how are you ever going to get all those tiny rollers in at the right angles?

A permanent wave will dry out your hair just as much as a colouring agent, so if you need a perm, have it done before you have it coloured, otherwise the chemicals used in the perm may react on the colouring chemicals, and your hair will be discoloured.

Most women want a perm to give their hair more volume and body and, technically speaking, a perm actually increases the dimension of each hair shaft, giving your hair more bulk.

I've had perms, both when my hair was very short and when it was very long, and in both cases I didn't find it an advantage. It waved my hair but, in order to style it, I had to set it every time it was washed, otherwise it just looked fuzzy. At least when it's straight, I can just wash and wear it.

Hair Washing

Before you read another sentence, look at the bottle of shampoo on the side of the bath. Is it the same brand that was there five years ago? Then chuck it out, because in those days shampoos were formulated to last a week or ten days, in between visits to the hairdresser's; but today most of us look after our own hair and wash it a lot more often. I've been washing mine daily since I was a teenager, and it hasn't hurt my hair one bit.

What is important is the type of shampoo you use. I used to think it didn't make any difference, and would buy the cheapest brand I could find; then I went on a hair seminar and tested a lot of samples, and realized just how much difference there really is. Now I have one favourite: Vidal Sassoon Shampoo. If I use any other kind my hair doesn't look as shiny, or feel as soft, so it must be doing something right.

The most important thing if you wash your hair often is to choose a shampoo with as low a detergent content as possible. One thing you must never use, however dire the emergency, is a cake of regular soap. I did once, and I thought I'd never get the resulting film out, and it didn't dissolve the dirt and oil either. The correct shampoo must be used for the appropriate hair type (dry, greasy, etc.). It's impossible to wash your hair properly without a spray attachment on either a basin or bath. Pouring cups of water over your hair is both slow and inadequate.

Conditioners and rinses are the most extraordinary things; they have lots of protein in them to supplement the amount you're already getting in your diet, and they plump out the hair shaft and smooth down the minuscule transparent scales on the hair cuticle so that it doesn't tangle when you comb it. The light reflects off the smoothness, and that's what makes your hair look shiny.

Fine hair tangles without a cream conditioner, but some conditioners leave hair feeling slightly sticky, no matter how often you rinse. For me the best on the market is the Vidal Sassoon Finishing Rinse, but test and test until you find the one that's right for you. Remember, you want to condition your hair, especially the dry ends, not your scalp.

If you ever find yourself without a rinse, you can use fresh lemon juice if you're a blonde; or cider vinegar for red highlights on a brunette head. Use about a third of a cup and dilute it, then rinse thoroughly in clean water.

1 Comb or brush through your hair to remove tangles or knots. Always start from the ends of the hair, and work towards the roots.

2 Wet your hair thoroughly with warm but not very hot water. Use as little shampoo as will give you a good coating. Pour it into your hands, and then work it in vigorously.

3 Massage your scalp, but make sure you don't scratch it with your fingernails, rinse well.

4 Soap again with an even smaller dollop of shampoo. Be sure you really clean your scalp, and your hairline, including the nape of your neck, which is where dirt and oil build up.

5 Now rinse until your hair squeaks when you pull a strand between two fingers. When you think your hair is totally free of soap, go on rinsing for one more minute. If there's even the

smallest speck of soap left, it's going to make your hair look dull and listless.

6 With your hand, squeeze your hair to get out most of the water. Then put a tiny amount of cream rinse on your hands and apply to mid lengths and ends of the hair. Never put it on a fringe, or hair that falls across your face as that will pick up oil anyway during the day from your skin. Thirty seconds later, gently comb through with a big, wide-toothed comb. Don't use a brush on wet hair. The comb will glide through the conditioned hair like butter, but then rinse again until it feels as if your scalp must be waterlogged.

7 A good squeeze with your hand to get out the excess moisture, and then gently pat it dry with a towel.

Dandruff

Technically, dandruff is an excessive shedding of old scalp skin cells. You can suddenly develop it at any age, and for no apparent reason. It may be hormonal, emotional or just plain tiredness. Do not on any account ignore it; not just because it's there for everyone to see, but because it may be either a scalp problem or a symptom of a more serious illness.

A couple of times when I thought it was starting, I used Head and Shoulders Shampoo for two or three weeks, and it went away. Another excellent preventive that I remember as a child is called Selsun. If the dandruff doesn't clear up, take your head to a trichologist, and let him solve the problem.

Hair Equipment

I don't know how any woman can survive without a small hand drier. For years I've used the one made by Braun, because it runs on dual current which means I can plug it in anywhere in the world, and it only weighs ounces to carry about.

I recently discovered that some driers run at a much higher voltage, which means the hair dries more quickly.

1 Keep the drier moving continuously so that your hair doesn't get scorched. Test against the back of your hand placed on your head. If your hand doesn't burn, your hair won't either. The best distance is usually about six inches.

2 Use foam rubber or wire mesh rollers, and don't wind the hair too tightly.

3 Like most people, I have funny cowlicks which are clumps of springy hair growing in the opposite direction from the hair immediately next to it. Take them into account as you dry your hair.

To handle the three on my temples which stop my fringe from lying flat; I comb my hair in a basin shape, and put a strip of tissue across the fringe, anchoring it down with clips. I dry most of the moisture from the fringe, and then I make a parting on the left-hand side and comb my hair from left to right. I then anchor the tissue down again, and dry the entire head. When it is completely dry, I part the hair on the right, and comb my hair from right to left.

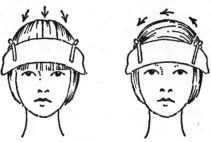

Hair drying

Combing and drying against the growth pattern gives volume. I don't know why, but if I let my hair dry naturally, it never looks as smooth and shiny.

Two alternatives to a drier are a hot comb and a curling iron. I've had long discussions with Clifford Stafford about their value, and he's very hesitant to recommend spending money on them. They are more expensive than a drier, and even though most of them are teflon coated, a moment's carelessness, and you may burn your hair. Another gadget I find cumbersome and inefficient is an old-fashioned bonnet drier.

Whatever equipment you buy, be sure you read all the instruction leaflets carefully and, if necessary, more than once; carelessness can be expensive.

Brushing

The main purpose of brushing is to stimulate blood circulation of the scalp. It frees tangles; lets fresh air get to your scalp, and works the natural oils down the shaft to give your hair lustre. However, brushing does activate the oil glands so if your hair is very oily, you should only use a comb.

The first decision to make is what kind of brush to use. Experts agree that natural bristles are superior, but there are also some excellent brushes of mixed natural and synthetic bristles. If you choose synthetic bristles, make sure the filaments are as smoothly rounded as the natural bristles. Sharp ends tear hair.

Depending on your hair type, do the following:

1   For thin, dry or brittle hair: handle with care. Comb out tangles first with a wide-toothed comb before gently brushing. Use only soft-bristled brushes.
2   If you have coloured, permed or straightened hair, boar bristles are the best. They distribute needed natural oils along hair shafts more effectively, thus combating the inevitable dryness.
3   For thick, curly hair, select a brush with long stiff bristles, then start your brushing close to the head. Work outwards towards the hair ends. This stimulates the scalp, and makes hair more manageable.
4   Treat fine hair with care; only brush once a day.
5   Be careful with oily hair, as over-stimulating the glands increases the oil flow.

When should you brush? Always before shampooing, so that the hair strands separate. Stiff or flattened hair can be fluffed up with a few light strokes by tipping your head forward and brushing up from underneath. Don't be afraid of energetic brushing after setting or styling. This adds a natural look and increases the shine. For normal hair, a good rule of thumb is to brush twice a day, twenty strokes a time.

However, there are times when you should go easy on the brushing. Never when your hair is wet as it loses elasticity and is easily damaged by breakage. If you want to style your hair with a hand drier, towel dry first so that most of the water is removed before you start working with a brush and drier.

Look after your brushes carefully. First, run another brush or a comb through the bristles to remove hairs. Then wash in luke-warm soapy water. Heat damages bristles, so don't dry them on radiators, in direct sunlight or with a blow drier.

Hair Colouring

I weighed up all the advantages and disadvantages of colouring my hair, and in the end decided that it's one of the things I don't want to spend money on. Whichever process you choose, it's not only the initial outlay but what comes after that adds up. I'll admit that millions of women colour their own hair, and it works well, but having it done professionally will cost a great deal over a year.

At least do me one favour: if you want your hair coloured, go to a top professional to begin with. You can always tell him you'd like to be able to do it yourself and need his advice. Consider carefully whether you're prepared to spend the time and money that's necessary for a proper maintenance programme.

One of these days I'll be faced with grey hairs, and then I may change my mind; but for now I'm satisfied with my own hair, in super condition and with a superb cut. Grey is as much a psychological colour as it is a physical one.

Technically speaking, there are three types of colouring techniques. The first, temporary colourants which last until they are shampooed out. They can be used on all types of hair, including bleached or tinted, to give subtle tones, or as a corrective measure, to tone down brassiness.

Semi-permanent colourants are designed to give stronger colour which will last through six to eight shampoos. They add colour tone to your natural shade. Some semi-permanent colours are specifically for use on grey or white hair and result in silver or pearl grey tones. They will never lighten the hair, and with normal use no regrowth is produced because the colour gradually washes out.

The third alternative is a permanent colourant, capable of either lightening or darkening. It's the perfect cover-up for grey or white hairs but, remember, your natural colour always influences the final result. Apply a brown tint to mid-brown hair, and the result is darker than if the same colour were applied to very light brown hair.

Once you have treated your hair with a permanent colour, the new shade cannot be removed by shampooing. It will only grow out, and then you will have to cope with touching up the roots.

1   If your hair is permed, you have to wait at least two weeks before you can use any type of colourant.

2   Coloured hair requires a lot of extra conditioning on a regular basis to combat dryness.

3   Go lighter, but never darker, as it accentuates the lines on your face, and attention is drawn to your hair colour instead of your features.

4   If you change your hair colour, be sure to change your make-up to match the new shade.

5   If you colour, don't leave your hair uncovered in the sun, as the ultra-violet rays react on the colouring chemicals; the only real protection is a straw hat.

Henna

Made from the leaves of an exotic herbal plant, henna adds shine, body and reddish glints to your hair if it's dark blond or darker. A safe, natural vegetable dye, it now comes in a wide range of shades, from light brown to mahogany and chestnut. There is even a colourless henna, and you can still choose the traditional red. What the paste does is to polish hair with highlights by coating each follicle, adding body and shine, the way a conditioner does, and helping to prevent split ends.

Made from the powdered leaves of a privet plant found in many Asian countries, henna is one of the oldest cosmetic colours known to civilization. When mixed with hot water, the powder forms a paste which is applied to the hair, left for about an hour, or half an hour when heat is used, and then shampooed out. Time of application depends on the base colour of the hair and the depth of shade required.

Most women find that henna gives their hair body, making it

easier to manage. You can use the colourless variety, made from the plant stems that give no colour, once a month, and get the conditioning benefits of the plant without the reddish effects.

One of the best things about henna colour is that the subtle hue fades away at the rate your hair grows, so there is never a problem of roots showing. And since henna treatments are always done all over the head, there is no need for touching up.

What it won't do is cover up grey hairs; and it's not recommended for light blond or white hair, or for hair that has been tinted or dyed. A professional trick is to mix strong coffee with natural henna for heavier colour.

I'm emphatic that henna should never be done at home. Not because it's dangerous, or you might harm yourself, but because it's the messiest gook I've ever touched in my life.

Do It Yourself; and your walls, your carpets, your clothes and your skin will all be stained. It really isn't worth it.

Wigs

If you think wearing a wig would simplify your life, it's up to you, but I can't understand why a good haircut wouldn't solve all your problems just as well.

There are two main objections I have to wigs: the first is that it's not natural, strokable or sexy; all three of which I think hair is, and must be; and secondly, any wig, either real hair or synthetic, makes your head perspire and mats your hair so that it is dank and stringy when you remove the wig. Is it worth the money?

If you're set on getting a wig, start by buying an inexpensive man-made fibre one, so that you can test it before investing in a handmade, all-European-hair one, which will probably cost at least £200. That would pay for a lot of good haircuts!

9 ❧ Looking After Your Body

Our Bodies

All of us are obsessed, to a greater or lesser extent, with our bodies. The lucky ones have to do the minimum to have it looking the way they want. Those whom fate didn't smile on quite as broadly have resigned themselves to a lifetime of discipline.

The key to everything is a realistic appraisal of which 'morph' you are; and it's easy enough to discover, since it's all about your bone structure:

Ectomorph: tall, narrow and long boned
Endomorph: soft, curved and voluptuous
Mesomorph: big-boned, broad-shouldered, in between the other two

Most of us are a combination of two, but it's totally impossible to change yourself into a shape that isn't yours by birthright.

More important than what you weigh is how you look. If your body is tight and toned up with exercise, you can get away with more weight on your frame. On the other hand, you could be so out of shape that even though you're the perfect weight for your height, you still have an abominable figure.

Work harder at being well proportioned than you do at being thin. Keep healthy because, if you're not, you won't have the energy to look after yourself. And, most important of all, like your body, because pride shows in the way you walk and hold yourself.

You know what the weight you can get to comfortably is; expand your energies to getting and staying there. It's supposed to be true that in our thirties our metabolism changes, and we don't get as hungry as when we're younger. What's important is to be supple, through exercise if necessary, and thin enough, so that clothes look good on you.

Ever since the Duchess of Windsor said that no woman can be too thin or too rich, this brittle little motto has been the creed of all the Beautiful People. But it's not quite true. Being very thin adds years to a woman's face. From about thirty-five on, a little bit of plumpness fills out the wrinkles, and keeps you looking young and desirable.

The fabulous thing about the human body is that every effort you make shows up for the world to see. Dieting can make a difference in a week or two: exercise can start to change your shape at the end of the first month. Giving up drink, drugs and cigarettes will start showing in seven days: and a new hair-do or make-up scheme is evident in hours.

If you want a really new You, what are you waiting for? Start now, and three months from now your best friend will have difficulty in recognizing you.

Exercise Clothes

Tights and a leotard are the only thing to wear when you're exercising. They show you not only what your body looks like, and how it is improving but, watching in the mirror, you'll be able to see how your body moves as you exercise.

Track suits and warm-up clothes are too baggy. They're not revealing enough to prove an incentive to you; a leotard will.

Exercise

I'm living, walking, talking proof that a proper exercise programme can rebuild a weak and flabby body. By the time the surgeons were finished with me, all the muscles and nerves in my back and stomach had been cut, and I was not only weak, but even more ungainly and unco-ordinated than usual, because I'd lost so much muscle control.

Then, two years ago, 'Granny's Beautiful Bodies' opened, and
Joan suggested I go along with her. The classes last an hour, with
the best part, a two-minute back rub and rest, coming half way
through. There are about a dozen women in each class; all different ages and sizes, but without a doubt, I was the worst! And
every so often Jo would politely suggest that I might like to sit this
next exercise out, so I wouldn't hold up the rest of the class.

Well, being bad at things makes me very stubborn and I started
going more often, three or four times a week and, suddenly, for the
first time in my life, I began to be quite good at simple gymnastics,
and I even began to like it; well, not a lot, but at least a little. I
still try to go two or three times a week, and if I skip it for even a
week or two, my back tightens up, my bulging tum flops forward
and my posture sags.

Some people think it's very un-British to go to an exercise class,
that it's lightweight stuff. Some of my friends are real tennis nuts,
who like the competitiveness of beating everyone else while they're
keeping their bodies in shape; but I'm not a female jock; I can
never win at games; and exercising is a very private matter between me and my body.

I don't have the self-discipline necessary to do exercises on my
own, at home. It's so easy to find an excuse not to get started; and
even though it's a bus ride to get to Granny's, it has become a
necessity in my life.

When I started exercising, I didn't go on any great diet, but I
did begin to be more aware when I was stuffing my face with junk,
and my weight stopped fluctuating so much. Now I quite con-
tentedly sit at nine stone, which is all right; and a stone lighter
than I was at twenty-five.

I have lost an amazing amount of inches all over, especially in
problem areas, and I'm sure regular exercise makes me less tense.
Nicest of all, I've discovered protruding hip bones under my
clothes, for the first time ever.

However much I still hate exercise, I know that at the end of
that hour I'm going to feel physically better, and my body will be
that much more limber. A class is also reassuring because you see
other people who are suffering even more, and it may sound cruel,
but it's a salutary lesson to discover how many worse bodies than
my own there are in the world.

Anything that gets you up and about, your circulation going, is good for you. Walking is better than going by bus; jogging is more healthy than a stroll; swimming tones up all your muscles. Choose what suits you best. Never do anything you don't enjoy, or it becomes a punishment with little pleasure, and even less rewards.

1   It's much better to do ten minutes every day, than an hour once a week. It's a great deal easier to exercise on an empty stomach, especially with the yoga breathing-based exercises I'm going to explain; so do your exercising first thing every morning; come Hell or High Water!

2   Never lie on the bed to exercise. The mattress is too yielding, and doesn't support your back properly.

3   If you're exercising on your own; work out on a bath towel in front of a big mirror, so that you're able to check, and correct, your movements. It's also a great incentive as you see your body gradually changing shape.

4   As you exercise, concentrate on each movement, and what it is doing to what part of your body. Try for the maximum effort each time, but never strain or force anything. If you ache at the end, you're overdoing it; but you should feel a definite pull as you move a muscle, otherwise you're not making it work hard enough.

5   Have music playing to relax you.

The following are the exercises I learned at Granny's. They are all based on this very simple breathing movement: you breathe in to prepare, and as you breathe out, you move. It may take weeks to make the breathing automatic as it is contrary to how we normally breathe, except in our sleep when we are at our most relaxed. Don't worry, one day you'll suddenly discover you're doing it without thinking about it.

Tights and leotard on: bath towel on the floor in front of the mirror.

1   Lie down on your back; bend your knees, feet flat on the floor, slightly apart. Place your hands on your stomach. Inhale deeply and expand your stomach so that it pushes hard against your hands. Hold for a count of two, and then blow out through your mouth, until your stomach flattens under

your hands, and becomes concave. Repeat eight times. Do it slowly, and listen to how hard you are breathing, making your lungs work. This not only relaxes you, it helps strengthen the stomach muscles.

2 Sit up straight on the floor: legs straight out in front of you, feet flexed. Put your clasped hands under your right knee. As you breathe out, lift your very taut leg, leading with the heel so there is a pull on the back of the leg. Bend your elbows to get more leverage and keep your back as straight as you can. Do six times on each leg. For hamstrings. A good warm-up.

3 Sit up straight on the floor: legs straight out in front of you, feet flexed. Lift both arms to the ceiling, and then arch your back as you bend forward reaching beyond your toes. Repeat six times, and on the last one, clasp your ankles, or the

bottoms of your feet, and the next four times you blow out, and flatten your stomach, bend your elbows so that your forehead hits your knees. For the hamstrings and the back.

4 Lie flat, knees bent, your feet apart, and slightly turned in. Place both hands on your stomach. Inhale and feel the rib cage and stomach expand. Exhale and tilt your bottom forward so that your bottom and thigh muscles are very tight. Really concentrate on your lower back, and if you're doing it hard enough, your thighs should shake. Repeat five times. For the lower back and to strengthen stomach muscles.

5 Lie flat, knees bent, your feet apart and slightly turned in. Hands are under your head. As you breathe out, slowly raise your hips off the floor. Control it by pressing your thighs tightly together, and straighten your spine and lift your pelvis until your weight rests on your shoulders and feet. Do four times, then hold for a count of two in a raised position. Inhale, and as you exhale, push your knees, thighs and heels together tightly. Good for aligning the spinal column, the back, buttocks, stomach and inner thighs.

6 Lie flat, knees bent to chest, hands at side. Breathe out, and swing your legs and hips straight up in the air, moving your hands to support your hips. Pedal twenty times forward, then twenty times back.

7 Kneel on all fours, balancing your weight between your hands and knees. As you exhale, curve your back, tuck your chin into your neck and draw your right knee up to your fore-head; on the next exhale, straighten out the leg behind you, toes pointed, lifting it, straight kneed, as high as you can. Do five times, and then repeat on the other leg. For the bottom.

8 Kneel on floor with knees together. Buttocks rest on heels, hands rest on knees, keep your eyes on your stomach. Breathe out completely, and tuck your stomach in as far as it will go. Hold for a count of six while you rapidly pull in the stomach muscle. Repeat five times. For the stomach, and for breathing control.

9 Sit cross legged, hands resting on knees. Bend your head forward, then roll to the right, trying to touch your right ear to your right shoulder without lifting the shoulder up. Backwards so the base of the skull touches the nape of the neck, and then left ear to left shoulder. End up with chin forward into chest as at start. Do three times, and then repeat, going to the left. For neck, shoulders and face.

10 Sit with legs bent, soles together. Clasp hands around feet and, as you exhale, bend slowly forward so that your forehead touches the ground. Hold, and then slowly come up as you exhale. Repeat five times. For inner thighs.

11 Sit up straight, legs straight out in front of you; toes flexed. Arms are stretched out in front. As you exhale, to a count of ten, slowly lower yourself to the floor, vertebra by vertebra. Bring arms down last, and place them by your side. Rest on the inhale, and then as you exhale, arms straight up in the air; come up to a count of ten. Move smoothly and don't jerk. If you have trouble coming up, put your hands under your thighs and pull up. Do five times. For stomach.

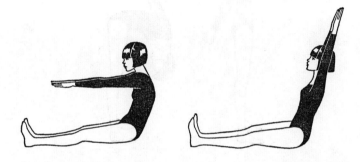

12 Stand up straight with your legs apart. Hold your right arm up in the air, and your left one straight down by your side. On the exhale, bend to the left, so that arm slides down your left leg, and the right arm crosses over your head. Come up straight on the inhale, and do six times. Repeat on the other side. For waist, hips and arms.

13 Stand up straight with your legs apart. Clasp your hands behind your back and bend forward, lifting your arms up behind you, as you exhale. Straighten up as you inhale. Do six times. For posture, arms and spine.

14 Stand up straight with your arms stretched straight up. On the exhale bend forward and let your arms swing between your legs, pushing as far behind you as you can get them. Repeat three times. On the last one, flop forward, weight on

the balls of your feet, arms dangling; no tension in head, neck or arms. Take a deep breath; and on exhale, raise your body very slowly.

That's Leslie's Big 14. Do all of them – or the ones that specifically work on your problem spots; that's up to you, but it's important to do each movement well, rather than rushing to get through them all.

Relax; breathe properly; and keep your feet flexed. 'Here's looking at you, kid,' as Bogart said to Bergman in *Casablanca*.

Posture

Bad posture is a horrible crime you commit against your body. You can erase five pounds, and at least that many years, just by standing up straight; and it doesn't cost a penny.

Because I was always a very tall child, I started hunching my shoulders early, so that at least one boy in dancing class would be higher than my breast bone. What finally improved my posture, many years later, was going regularly to exercise class. As my body became more supple, it became automatic to stand up straight.

1 Stand in front of the mirror with a leotard on. Pull your neck up out of your shoulders, hold your chin parallel to the floor and look straight ahead.
2 Exhale and suck in your stomach so that it falls back naturally, then tuck your bottom under. Don't tip your body either forward or backward, but stand firmly, carrying your weight on the balls of your feet.
3 Breathe deeply and stretch; now fall back into the proper position, profile to the mirror, and watch as you pull your body up. Do this every morning for two minutes until standing correctly is an automatic reflex.

Walking

The way you walk is so automatic that I bet you never even think about it; but in fact an ungainly walk can make a beautiful woman unattractive, and a beautiful walk can make you forget a homely woman isn't, technically speaking, good looking.

Years ago I met Diana in Nassau. She was a very attractive brunette with grown-up daughters, but when she moved it was absolutely mesmerizing, and no one in the room could take their eyes off her. She moved like some wonderful jungle creature; all smooth and gliding. I've never been able to achieve the perfection of Diana's walk, but I was taught to do the model's glide years ago for a fashion show, and all it takes is a little practice.

1   Set up one mirror so that you can see yourself walking towards it, and another at an angle so that you'll see yourself walking away.

2   Stand up straight, blow out your breath so that your stomach is empty and then pull it in tight. Constrict your bottom muscles very tightly, and push your pelvis slightly forward.

3   Now start to walk. With the right foot going forward all the way from the top of the hip bone.

4   At first you'll feel as if you're tilting backwards, but that's exactly it. Put down your toe before flattening out your foot and letting your heel touch the ground. Until it's absolutely automatic, keep your toe slightly pointed so that you don't forget it hits the ground first. Also try to keep your feet pointing straight ahead, never let them turn in.

5   As long as you keep your pelvic area properly tucked in, the legs will follow along. Once you've got it down pat; the top half of your body won't bounce around at all.

6   Keep your hands very close to your sides, and only let them swing a few inches in front of, or behind, your body. Left hand with right foot forward, and vice versa. To look more graceful, close your hand into a slight fist, so that your thumb lies on top of four folded fingers, and as you walk it's pointing downwards.

In the beginning, all this will feel very contrived, but with a little practice, it will become second nature. Practice whenever you're walking down the street, and soon you'll be doing it without ever having to think about it.

Not only will you find yourself walking like a gazelle, but it's a great trick to strengthen your stomach muscles.

Massage

One of the greatest pleasures in life. Except for sex, it is the best
tension reliever I've ever encountered; but on its own massage
won't make much of a change in your figure.

If you are dieting, and keeping to a rigorous exercise programme, it is an additional aid in keeping your muscles and skin
taut and firm. It helps stimulate the circulation, and that's also
good for you. It can't hurt, it can help, but make it only one part
of your body care programme.

Cellulite

I don't care how many male authorities pontificate that there is no
such thing as cellulite, I've got it on my thighs, and I haven't yet
discovered anything that makes it go away.

Cellulite's technical description is: 'fatty tissue that holds fat,
water and wastes in clumps on the upper arms, thighs, bottom,
hips or stomach'. If you notice an orange peel effect in those areas,
that's because of the shape of the hair follicles on the skin, rather
than the cellulite itself.

My experience is that once you've got it, you're stuck – but to
improve it as much as possible get plenty of exercise; strongly
massage the affected area; eat lots of raw fruits and vegetables;
increase elimination by drinking lots of water; and eat high fibre
foods. Cut out sugar products and high calorie foods as well as all
salt from your diet, as it helps to retain water between the cells.

Nudity

Since the mid-sixties, we've all been living in a world of increased
nudity, and I can't say I find it wonderfully exciting and erotic.
The truth is that 99·9 per cent of us look better when clothed; and
nothing on earth is as unexciting as complete nudity, unless you
are in your bedroom with someone you love and desire.

A very stylish Frenchman was once quoted as saying that his
countrymen preferred shaded lights to naked bulbs, and I think
seeing any body that is too thin, too fat or too old is painful. Never
expose flesh unless it is firm and young, and that doesn't just mean

sagging breasts and flabby thighs; crêpy-skinned bare arms can be as obscene as a blue film.

The theory of shifting erogenous zones has been operating for hundreds of years. Fashion fixes it so that we reveal only one section of our bodies at a time. When society is bored with legs, the bosom is unveiled, when men are tired of ankles, a suddenly bared shoulder will look surprisingly erotic.

I think wearing a transparent shirt is ugly; but a silk shirt, worn without a bra, can be modestly revealing, and a subtle turn on.

Body Hair

This is one of those rarely discussed, intimate problems which causes great distress to many women. They think they are the only ones suffering from it, when in fact, heavy hair growth on some part of the body is almost universal. The use of hormones in pills and creams has also affected the rate of hair growth over the last fifteen years.

I hate the look of body hair, and I have tested electric razors, straight razors, bleaching and electrolysis. I settled for waxing my legs, forearms and underarms. It is expensive having it done professionally, but eventually it weakens the hair so that you need do it less often. Don't do it at home; it is a messy business, as well as a great deal more painful to pull off the wax yourself. I've learnt from experience that your relationship with your beauty operator affects the amount you suffer. For years, Sue looked after me at Elizabeth Arden, and we were so busy gossiping, that I never noticed the sting.

An astonishing thing is that the rate of regrowth varies widely on different parts of the body. For days the skin is beautifully soft and smooth, and then sufficient regrowth has to come in before it's done again, or else the wax won't take hold. After waxing, little red pin-prick marks may appear, and last for a matter of hours. Rub on lots of body lotion and they disappear overnight.

I have to wax every:

2 weeks, under arms
4 weeks, arms
4–5 weeks, legs

Looking After Your Body

For a soft down on your shoulder blades, between your breasts, on your stomach, or on your forearms that is noticeably dark, bleach with Nestle Lite Hair Lightener.

Shaving is probably the most widespread way to remove hair, but stubble reappears after twenty-four hours, so it's a constant chore.

Safety Razor:

1 Use a good shaving foam, and soak in a warm bath first to help soften the hairs.
2 Be sure the blade is ultra sharp, or you'll scrape yourself unnecessarily.
3 Have your own razor and don't borrow your man's. Try one of the new skinny shapes which are specifically designed to fit female curves.
4 Clear off the foam after every stroke, or it will get too clogged up to give you a clean shave.
5 Shave against the direction in which the hair grows.
6 Wash off all the foam, and rub in a good body lotion when you're finished.

Electric Razor:

1 Be sure your skin is completely dry.
2 Use either a buffer coat of powder, or one of the special pre-electric shave conditioners to smooth your way.
3 Gently run the razor all over your skin in small circular strokes. Don't drag it across your skin.
4 Wash off all the powder or shaving lotion. Pat on body lotion.

Electrolysis is the only permanent hair removal there is; not the first time you have it done, but after a varying number of treatments. On some parts of the body it's completely painless, on others there's a real jab. It's never unbearable, and the result is fabulous. It removes hairs on your breasts, or between them; on your stomach; and on the bikini line. If it does hurt a lot; before starting, hold an ice cube against the skin until it feels a little numb. I just read a magazine and don't notice it.

If any hairs become ingrown after shaving or waxing, scrub

hard with a loofah or Buf-Puf whenever you take a bath, and it usually brings them up through the surface.

There are also a number of depilatory creams on the market, and they're supposed to last longer than shaving. Be sure to test carefully before you use one. They are chemicals after all; one that's right for your legs may be much too strong for your face.

Perspiration

Whenever we're physically overheated, or emotionally tense, the pores of our body open up so that moisture can escape and cool us down as it evaporates on the skin surface.

Perspiration exudes an unpleasant smell only when it combines with the bacteria already on the skin surface. Washing as often as necessary removes the bacteria, but in order to stop perspiration under your arms, use an anti-perspirant which both stops the flow of moisture and deodorizes.

Years ago, I was interviewing Barbra Streisand before a big outdoor concert, and she mentioned, as she was changing into her stage costume, that everyone in the theatre used Mitchum's Anti-Perspirant because it worked more effectively than any other. I've used it ever since. No longer an underground theatrical secret, it's now available at every good chemist.

When it's very hot, only wear natural fibre fabrics, as they absorb moisture and cool down the body. Synthetics are horribly hot and sticky, and trap the moisture back against your skin surface.

Never use an anti-perspirant if you're wearing a dark coloured shirt or dress, as the chemicals in it will leave a white mark on the fabric.

You can perspire almost as heavily during cold weather if you are wearing heavy clothing and going into hot rooms, but you may prefer to use only a deodorant. Removing underarm hair also helps to cut down on the perspiration flow.

Pregnancy

I've never given birth, so I can't speak from experience, but friends have pointed out the big change in the thinking about pregnancy over the last fifteen years. No longer is it fashionable to say that for nine months you're going to sit around being lazy and getting fat.

Self-indulgence won't help you or the baby, so be practical and don't overeat, or stop exercising. The more you look after your body now, the less difficult it will be to get back into shape after the birth.

1 Never wear a maternity girdle as it weakens your muscles and you'll take much longer tightening them up again.

2 To avoid stretch marks massage your stomach and thighs after your bath and before you go to sleep with any cream that has collagen in it. Stretch marks come from any weight change under the skin's surface, and the mark itself is the surface effect of a break in your body's collagen fibre. Prenatol is an overall body lotion recommended for pregnant women.

3 Pay special attention to your feet. Whenever you can, sit back with your feet up, and before you get into bed at night massage your feet with cream and unknot all the tendons.

4 Start abdominal exercises just as soon as your doctor will let you. If you're healthy and have kept yourself in good shape, it may be as soon as twelve hours after the birth. Swimming and bicycling are the best sports for you.

Keeping Clean

I save a fortune on not going to a psychiatrist because I use the bath to give me the same feeling of security and relaxation. It's really a primeval feeling of returning to the womb.

Unless you have low blood pressure, which means you can't soak in hot water without getting exhausted, I think a warm bath is the best ten minutes in the day. A time to relax, to unwind, to pull yourself together.

It's very hard to judge for yourself if the water where you live is hard or soft but if, after you come out of the water, your skin is dry and flaky, consider it as hard. There are ways to soften your bath water which makes it easier to remove the soap and dirt as you wash. You can buy lots of expensive bath oils; my favourites are

Frühmesner Bade Öl, or Penhalgion's Hammam Oil; but when I'm feeling poor, I buy Borax Powder at the chemist's, and toss a couple of tablespoonfuls into the water.

I hang a lavender bag from the tap, so that the hot water runs into it and suffuses the room with the scent. I take a magazine or newspaper with me (it tends to fall in the water, so books are banned), and I lie back for a few minutes, leaning my head against a folded-up towel while my muscles unwind.

When you're completely relaxed, lather soap all over, and scrub everywhere with a Buf-Puf. A good hard rub with a soapy pumice stone on the water-softened skin on your soles and heels; an over-all rinse of clean water and you're out, folding yourself into a big bath towel. While you're still faintly damp, put on heavy slatherings of body lotion.

If you have ever had cystitis, don't use any oils or special rinses in the water. The chemicals in them are bad for your condition; but use lots of body lotion when you get out, to counteract the effect of hard water on your skin.

I'm very mean about spending money on expensive body lotions: I use whatever I find on sale or special offer; and the best inexpensive one I've found is Vasoline Intensive Care Lotion. I steer clear of any glycerine product. Glycerine needs moisture so much that, if there's none in the air, it draws it out of your skin.

If you've overdone the exercise, and your muscles ache; pop a handful of aspirins into the hot water and soak.

Showers get you clean, but I don't think they're as much fun. You decide.

10 ❧ Dieting

The Health Farm Fast

Within a month of moving to London, one of the big women's magazines sent me to Hampshire to report on the Forest Mere Health Hydro. There were times when I would have sold my fat body for a chocolate bar; but at the end of the week I had lost half a stone; the daily massage had tightened up the flab; and I felt terrific, imbued with the determination to eat only healthy foods in the future. I've managed to get two more assignments to health farms, but I could never afford to pay the £100 a week on my own behalf.

Instead, three or four times a year when I need to start a diet, I do a weekend at home, based on what I learned at Forest Mere. It's a lot easier to begin dieting with a radical cooling-off period, and I like the idea of cleaning out my system and starting from scratch. On my first visit to Forest Mere, I got headaches after a day of fasting, a natural sign that toxins are being flushed out of your system. That's one of the reasons I always fast on a weekend; the other being that it's the only time I can pamper myself.

Treat yourself to a sybaritic mini holiday by following these twelve easy rules.

1 Friday night unwind: read, watch television. Eat whatever you want, and when you're tired, go to sleep. No spirits, no pills and, after midnight, nothing to eat.
2 Saturday morning, sleep as late as you want. No pressure, no rush. When you're finally completely awake, weigh yourself, naked. Then make yourself a mug of hot water with one tablespoon of pure lemon juice. It can be either freshly

squeezed or PLJ. Drink this as hot as possible and back to bed with the papers.

3 Put on tights and a leotard; and in front of a full-length mirror, do your exercises. Slowly, leisurely, thirty minutes of stretching and unkinking all your muscles.

4 Reward for all this effort is a cup of hot herbal tea, or another mug of hot lemon water. Whichever you prefer. Treat yourself to small packs of different herbal teas until you find the ones you like. I enjoy peppermint and rose hip; but some of the others are decidedly medicinal. Take your drink with you into the bath, into which you have poured a capful of your favourite bath oil. Lie back, listen to the radio, turn off the lights and daydream till you feel as if you've turned into a prune. Pat yourself dry, smooth on lots of body lotion, and finish off with dusting powder.

5 Back to bed with a pile of books and magazines. Listen to music, watch an old film on television. If you feel drowsy, take a nap. The thought of there being nothing you have to do is very relaxing. Mid-afternoon, have another cup of herbal tea. On a fast, never cheat with a cup of coffee or tea; taken straight, they may have no calories, but they do have caffeine, and that's a stimulant.

6 During the day, ward off hunger by drinking as much water as you want. I hate the taste of tap water, and Perrier is expensive, so I use my soda maker, and fill up with lots of soda water bubbles. Dinner is at 8 p.m.: a cup of hot vege-table bouillon made from stock cubes bought in the health food store, and one small container of plain unsweetened yoghurt, mixed with three teaspoons of bran. The yoghurt and bran give you a little texture to chew on, and will, surprisingly enough, fill you up.

7 Read or watch TV till you're sleepy, and then it's bed, without any pills to help you sleep.

8 If your system is full of toxins from cigarettes, spirits or drugs you may find yourself on Sunday morning with a foul taste in your mouth, and a headache. For the headache, take one paracetamol, but never plain aspirin, which may upset your stomach. For the foul taste, brush your teeth, and use a mouthwash.

9 Sleep as late as you can, and when you're awake, weigh yourself straight away. Hot water and lemon for breakfast, and after a long session with the Sunday papers, back on with the tights and leotard, and do your exercises before another hot bath.

10 Lunch is a cup of hot tomato juice, pepped up with a little lemon juice. Read, write letters, do a little sewing, anything that you find relaxing. Hot herbal tea about 5 p.m., and at 8 it's yoghurt and bran; and as a special reward for being so good all weekend, stir in a teaspoon of pure honey. The drink can be a herbal tea or, if you like, make another hot lemonade, and use your teaspoon of honey in this.

11 On Sunday night, go to sleep when you're tired; then start on Monday morning at your usual time. For breakfast, have three teaspoons of bran and a cup of black coffee with artificial sweetener. From now on for the rest of your life, always have a small daily portion of roughage with your morning coffee. Lunch is light, maybe yoghurt and honey or, if you're famished, an omelette. Dinner might be a plain piece of broiled fish or chicken and a green salad or, if the weather's hot, a big salad with lots of raw vegetables all chopped up.

12 Try to keep up this spartan regime for at least a week, by which time you'll have lost half a stone: but by midweek, if you're very busy and rushing around, increase what you eat, while still trying to stick to as much natural food as possible.

Dieting for me is sticking to 1000 calories a day, and the Fasting Weekend puts me in exactly the right frame of mind for this. My stomach shrinks, and what looked like a minuscule appetizer last week looks like a hefty main course this week. My body gets so bloated on an average diet, that just to have my stomach flatter makes me feel full of resolve and self-control.

Diet

The world is made up of two kinds of people: those who eat to live, and those who live to eat. I definitely belong to the second group. I was born greedy, and greedy I'll die. Every single day of my life is spent fighting temptation, and it's a battle that I constantly lose, sometimes more, sometimes less, depending on my emotions.

'Willpower, like a muscle, grows through use.' I've cut that out and taped it to the front of the fridge. Surprising what a help it is in not opening the door! All my emotions are linked directly from my mouth to my brain; when I feel fat, I also feel ugly, nasty and aggressive. I act like that too, which isn't very pleasant for the people around me.

At 'sweet sikteen' I was described as 'pleasantly plump', and hovered between 9½ and 10 stone, starving myself one month, and going on binges the next. At twenty-six I was up to 10½ stone, not completely my own fault as I was ill again; but when I look back at photographs I shudder. Great broad middle; round face without a cheekbone to be seen; ample poitrine giving me the look of a contented nursing mother.

At thirty-two my metabolism changed for no special reason that I know of; perhaps I was just a late developer; but for the first time I began to feel as if I was burning up more calories than I consumed. Now I can control my cravings more easily, and a healthy diet, allowing for a certain amount of cheating, keeps me within a three-pound swing of what suits my body best.

At 8 stone 11 pounds I feel skinny, sensual and energetic; at 9 stone I'm satisfied and my clothes look all right; at 9 stone 4 pounds I look and feel fat, with a protruding tum.

To diet, you can keep tabs on calories, grammes, or ounces; but it's all a waste of time as far as I'm concerned. The only infallible diet I have ever found is to put less food into my mouth. There isn't a fad diet I haven't experimented with in the last twenty years, but the best one is also the most simple, and I started it back in my *Glamour* days. I call it 'Leslie's Eat Lots Less Diet' (see end of chapter).

Whatever other people say; only you can judge what diet works best for you. For example, if I eat breakfast, it gives me an insatiable appetite for the rest of the day. So I start the day with nothing but black coffee. During the day I try to eat as little as possible because I'm always hungry at night, whether I've already had a big meal in the middle of the day or not.

Dieting

With every year, I try to eat a little less. On average we gain one pound for every birthday after twenty-five, and I can't afford to carry that increased weight around. I've given up all the things that don't really matter to my taste buds: I now take a sweetener instead of sugar; margarine instead of butter; grapefruit juice instead of orange; no salt on anything.

My problem is not that I like foods that are bad for me, it's that I like such large quantities of everything; that word 'greedy' again. No food of any sort is bad for you unless you eat it to excess or you have a particular allergy. Good nutrition is nothing more complicated than 'eating not too much of a balanced variety of foods at regular intervals'.

In 100 per cent of overweight cases, food intake exceeds energy expenditure. Simple solution then: 3500 calories is equal to a pound of body weight; so the Number One rule is obvious: eat less and exercise more. I may not like it; but it does work. It's hard to diet and it's unpleasant but oh boy, do I like the result!

You must decide the best weight for yourself. You know at what point you feel skinny or fat; when you think you look good or when you don't. Taste is acquired, if you find that you're eating all sorts of foods which don't do much good for your hair, eyes, nails and skin, let alone your weight, re-educate your 'appestat'. Unlearn bad habits and teach yourself to enjoy foods that are good for you: clean, natural, healthy foods, instead of ones that are sweet and starchy.

If both your parents are overweight, it's easy to think you've inherited a weight problem from them; but it's far more likely that your family just has bad eating habits. I was brought up by a nanny whose golden rule was always 'clean your plate for the poor starving children in China'. This suited my greedy nature perfectly, but I wasn't smart enough to question what good my clean plate was doing those slant-eyed waifs. In fact, the most useful thing I could have been taught would have been to leave the table with my stomach only half full.

Calorie burning goes on every minute of the day; even when you're asleep you're using up half a calorie per pound of body weight per hour. It's so much easier to lose three pounds than it is thirteen that your main diet objective may only be prevention and maintenance. Keep tabs on your weight; weigh yourself every morning, and take off that extra pound as it appears.

Since I find it absolutely impossible not to eat between meals, I tend when I'm writing at home to nibble, but I never sit down to a substantial meal. I try and make sure that the things I eat aren't all carbohydrates and starch; but at the start of a diet, don't throw out a cupboard of goodies because you know you shouldn't eat them, if the health foods you replace them with are only going to sit on the shelf. When you cheat, and you will (at least I always do), enjoy it. Don't gobble down forbidden fruits, feel guilty, and not take time to savour how good they taste.

Controlling my weight is a life-long discipline that started the day I was born, and will continue till the day I die. It's no good playing Scarlett O'Hara and saying, 'I'll think about it tomorrow', because tomorrow may be too late. You may have dozens of reasons for reducing, the only one I need is that I hate my body when I'm fat. I've always joked that I only have to look at a cream bun for it to appear on my hips. I don't talk much about dieting to other people, not only because it's the most boring topic in the world, but because I don't think it's any of their business if I go ahead and cheat a little.

If I could, I'd always be three pounds under my 'good' weight; it makes me a little edgy, a little hyped up, and it gives me an excess of nervous energy that I like. Harriet and I have often discussed this sort of hypertension, but try as we might, neither of us has been able to find the trigger that sets it off at will. It either comes from going through a nervous emotional crisis, or from diet pills, which I think are a dangerous false crutch, affecting your hormone balance.

If I were very overweight, had tried everything including joining Weight Watchers and couldn't find a way to control my appetite, rather than use drugs I'd be fat and forget it. But a doctor is the only person who can properly advise you, and for any weight gain or loss over a stone, I beg you to get proper medical supervision.

Every beauty book I've ever read says you must drink a minimum of eight glasses of water a day, and that's in addition to any other liquid intake. I don't, and I never have. I was born with a strong aversion to water, the taste makes me gag, and it leaves a funny feeling in my stomach. I reckon that I compensate by eating lots of fresh fruits and vegetables which have liquids in them. My body is clever enough to let me know when it's dehydrated, and it rarely does, so I don't worry about it. I never cook with, or put salt on, my food, which helps control my thirst. Most of us get between six and ten times as much salt in our daily diet as we need, and many women complain about water retention as an excuse for not losing weight.

Vitamins

Even though all of us succumb to junk food at times, most of us do eat with reasonable care. That means we probably get all the vitamins we need from what we eat. Just to make sure, I take one of the Boots Plurivite M – multiple vitamins with iron – with my morning cup of coffee.

In the winter I also swallow a Vitamin C tablet, believing in the Dr Linus Pauling theory that if you take a large dose of Vitamin C every day it protects you from colds. I think it works, and I'd rather prevent than have to cure.

1 Don't worry about taking too many vitamins. Most of them are water soluble, so your body throws off what it doesn't need.

2 If you smoke, have a Vitamin C tablet every day, as tobacco destroys it in your system.

3 If you're taking any kind of hormone pill, take Vitamin E supplement because the hormones destroy E.

4 Don't peel apples, pears or potatoes, but wash them well. Most of their vitamins are stored in the skin, so what's the use of throwing them all away?

'Leslie's Eat Lots Less Diet'

BREAKFAST	LUNCH	DINNER	SNACKS
a medium-size glass of grapefruit juice: or a grapefruit half: or a piece of melon	a broiled three-ounce hamburger: or 2 hard-boiled eggs: or a tin of water-packed tuna fish	a small glass of either tomato or grapefruit juice	hard-boiled eggs
			carrot sticks
		two broiled lamb cutlets: or a small fillet steak: or half a broiled chicken: or a three-ounce hamburger: or some roast lamb: or roast beef	tomatoes
one or two boiled or poached eggs	a raw tomato, and two raw carrots		celery
			cucumbers
			skimmed milk
			grapefruit juice
			tomato juice
tea, or black coffee with artificial sweetener	tea, or black coffee with artificial sweetener	spinach: or runner beans: or broiled tomatoes	soda water with a dash of lemon juice
			small container of plain yoghurt
		lettuce with lemon juice and vegetable oil dressing	piece of hard cheese
		half a grapefruit	

11 ✣ The Do It Yourself Make-Over

The Do It Yourself Make-Over

Think about what lies ahead as a battle plan, and to begin with, clear a day for yourself. Farm out the kids if you have them, send your husband off to chat up a client, or at least his mother. If you're footloose and fancy free, it's easy, 'book yourself out' as the models say, and begin the new you now.

Equipment

Beauty Book: Any change you make, whether it's half a pound lost, or half an inch disappeared, deserves a record, so first of all get yourself a small notebook to record your achievements in. Whether it's covered in leather, paper or fabric, choose one you like so that it's a treat to keep it up to date. I happen to have a passion for clean sheets of paper, and love the precision of ruling boxes and charts. For your eyes only, the written record will tabulate your progress, where you started, and where you get to.

Tape Measure: Keep it tucked in your beauty book so no one else bags it.

Bathroom Scale: One that is accurate with an easily readable face. Weigh yourself first thing every morning, naked, and before you've had so much as a sip of black coffee. Record the weight on your chart. If you're dieting, up even a pound means you have to cut something out today. If your scale isn't 100 per cent perfect it doesn't matter, so long as you always weigh yourself on the same scale. That way, it's a reliable guide as to what's happening.

Mirrors: Even your very best friend, bound to you by endless shared confessions and escapades, isn't your best friend if you're competition. Mothers are no help either, they all want their little girl to look like a sweet innocent. Only you can choose what's right for you.

The best, the only, way to discover yourself is to look in the mirror. But you're not just taking an ordinary perfunctory look, you're about to study yourself with the unswerving glare of your most bitter enemy. A three-way mirror shows you what other people see, what your rivals see, and don't you want to be as well informed as they are? Try to look at yourself as a stranger, not the way you always thought you looked. You have to see yourself to know yourself.

Estée Lauder always says that your mirror is your best friend, and I know exactly what she means. No hidden jealousies; no emotions; the mirror reveals exactly what is there, neither more nor less.

Study yourself in the mirror every time you dress to go out. Then, once you know everything is perfect, forget about your looks and concentrate on having a good time.

Construct an inexpensive two-way system by hanging one mirror on the wall, and another full-length one on the inside of a cupboard door so that you can move it about.

Always say, do I look perfect? I usually dress to please the man of the moment, but even though men are quick to say 'I like', they're very inarticulate about what it is they like. The only sure thing I've figured out is that they prefer the subtle to the flagrant. Even if they do spot a defect, they wouldn't know how to correct it. When I ask, 'how do I look?' I'm not really asking for an objective judgement, what I want is instant approval.

The Do It Yourself Make-Over

Now we come to the worst voluntary hour you may ever have to spend. Even if it's all 'do it yourself' and not a posh beauty salon, the boost to your morale in pampering yourself is worth it. Even if it's only an hour every week, save it and set it apart to spend time on yourself. I regard the time spent on looking after my body as an investment. What matters is how you look, not how you got that way.

The time and tears, the depression when nothing seems to happen quickly enough, are all forgotten when the results begin to show; and after a while self-discipline becomes easier. There's not a single figure problem I can think of that can't be minimized, or changed, and keeping your body in good shape is the most economical shortcut I know. The pleasure you'll take in yourself is just the start of your reward.

The Make-Over Test: Part 1

1 Are you wearing your hair in a different style from the one you had five years ago?

2 Have you had a professional haircut in the last six weeks?

3 Is your hair colour as bright and healthy looking as it was two years ago?

4 Have you bought a new 'going out to dinner' dress in the last two years?

5 Has your skirt length changed in the last year?

6 Are you using any make-up that you didn't use a year ago?

7 Are the colours on your face different from the ones you used six months ago?

8 Have you experimented with, or asked a question about, any new beauty product in the last six months?

9 Would you be upset if the man in your life said, 'you look just the same as the day we met'?

10 Would you be glad if your favourite man saw you in a leotard with no make-up on?

11 Do you put anything besides soap and water on your face?

12 Do you admire women who take care of their looks?

I get a score of twelve yeses when I take this test, but whatever your score the answers should make you think.

Part 2

Clean all make-up off your face and have a bath, not because you'll look different, but because it makes you feel good. Tie your hair away from your face and cover it with a scarf so that all you see is shape and bones.

Don't flinch, I promise you I know the agony of examining your body in broad daylight; every wart, every line, every sagging muscle shows. However little you decide you want to change, it won't happen overnight.

1   Do the flab test. Can you take a pinch of flesh between your thumb and forefinger on your thighs, stomach, rib cage, bottom and hips? If you can on three out of the five, a diet is in order.
2   Lie flat on the floor. Place a ruler down your side so that it touches your ribs and your hips. Does it hit anything in between? If it does, you're overweight.
3   Now put on a bikini, and place a straight chair in front of the mirror. Sit up straight on it. Does a paunchy abdomen show or a roll of flesh? Right; exercise and diet.
4   Stand up; hold in your stomach, tighten your buttocks, lift up your rib cage, stretch up your neck. How does it all look? When you breathe out, how far does it all sag?

Last test: stand back from the mirror, and walk towards it. Look at your reflection and then follow it away at an angle. For a little while be extremely self-conscious. What wobbles, what shakes?

Stand back and look at yourself inch by inch. Be generous, think, 'I like this, I like that; that has to go, this won't do.' There's almost nothing you can't change. Keep that in mind.

The Ideal

Whatever your height, whatever your weight, there is never only one ideal set of measurements for you. It's all got to do with the proportion between the different parts of you. To get a clear idea of how you look to others do the following experiment.

Get a large sheet of brown paper, which must be wider than

your hip measurements, and at least as tall as your height. Scotch tape or Blue Tac it to a wall, and stand flat against it, facing out, naked or with only a bathing suit on, and bare feet.

Make sure your heels, hips and shoulders, are against the wall. Outline your body with a felt tip pen. Hold your arm straight down, hand flat, one at a time. Step away and darken the outline.

Judge the trouble spots and you'll probably find things that are out of proportion or too obviously large, such as too-wide hips in proportion to your shoulders; too low a waist compared to the length of your thighs.

The Field Theory is that the best possible place to be long is in the thighs, which is exactly where most of us are stumpy. The way we look is all to do with the bones; if you've got very long narrow bones and a long neck, you can carry more weight and still look willowy. If you're short and curvy, being thin will make you smaller, but not a different shape. Exercise and weight loss will slim down heavy upper arms, flabby thighs, a thick waist, and Rubenesque hips.

Now get out your Beauty Book. Looking at photographs can be a revelation; so for this get a friend to help. To keep as a record you want: one full face head shot; one left profile; one right profile; and one full length showing you as you are today. Glue them right in the front of the book so you'll never forget where you started from.

A really cold-blooded examination of the pictures can be an eye-opener. Pretend you're looking at a stranger and criticize that figure as if it were someone else's. It's easier doing this with photographs than with a mirror, because stills focus on defects and make them more noticeable than when a face is constantly in motion. The camera has a tendency to flatten out the features, but what you correct for in photographs will pay off in real life as well.

Now your beauty book is begun, and it's going to record every change all your efforts make from this day forward. Don't expect perfection from yourself, or the times you gorge on sweets, or the exercise classes you skip will seem insurmountable sins. Don't waste time punishing yourself; just start again. I expect I cheat nearly as often as I keep to my beauty regime, but imagine what I would look like if I weren't good 50 per cent of the time.

Dedication and self-discipline are part of it, but achievement gives one an enormous feeling of satisfaction and increases the desire to keep at it. It's never too early to start good beauty habits, and it's certainly never too late to alter anything, not if you care enough.

I'm a great believer in setting goals for myself: not competition against the blonde on my left, or the redhead on my right, because I'll be so busy looking from side to side to see how they're doing that I'll soon be left behind. I'm practical enough to aim for things that are possible for me to achieve.

Day dreams are a big help. Think of what you want to look like more than anything in the world, and keep that picture in the back of your mind. A little fantasy will help get you through many a long hungry night. You'll never get anywhere if you don't know where it is you want to go.

Get out your tape measure and fill in this information on the next page of your book.

HEIGHT:
BUST:
WAIST:
STOMACH, 1 inch below the waist:
HIPS, across your navel:
RIGHT THIGH, at fattest place:
LEFT THIGH, at fattest place:
RIGHT CALF, at widest part:
LEFT CALF, at widest part:

Draw twelve vertical lines, and four weeks from this first day, measure yourself again. Put in the numbers next to the previous one; so month by month you can see any change.

Like every woman, some of my body is good, some bad, and some just all right. On the next page make two columns, Good and Bad. Start from the top of your head and objectively judge every part of your body. Be ruthless, and when the list is finished, the things on the Good list are what you'll dress and make-up to accentuate, and those on the Bad list are what you're going to change or camouflage.

GOOD	BAD
Shiny Hair	Baby Fine Hair
Big Eyes	Too Long Nose
Long Eyelashes, But Thin	Left Ear Sticks Out
Mouth, Turns Up at the Corners	Splotchy Complexion
	Eyebrows Are Completely Different Shapes
Small Hands	Nails Are Often Brittle and Break
Well-Shaped Nails	Convex Rib Cage
Nicely Shaped Breasts	Protuberant Tum
Small Waist	Fat Thighs, Cellulite!
Well-Shaped Calves	Bad Bump on Right Heel
Small Ankles	
Small Feet, High Arches	

You may find many of the same pluses and minuses on your list as well. The more I learn about women and their beauty problems, the more I realize that most of us have the same ones. Analyse your lists; the Good side is simple, it just requires maintenance. The Bad list sub-divides into two parts: things you can change by diet, exercise, make-up, or hairdressing skills, and those things you can't change so easily. I can only change my nose and left ear by plastic surgery and I don't have the courage, so I camouflage them and forget them. The bump on my heel is unfixable; I've tried, it didn't work, I forget it. The other problems I work at constantly.

On the next page, write down your weight every single morning. You may be surprised to see how much it can fluctuate.

Make-up

Face Equipment I can't live without

Headband to keep my fringe out of my eyelashes
Tissues
Cotton wool
Cotton buds
Assortment of brushes and sponge applicators: when make-up is used up I never throw away the applicator. It's washed and then used over and over again. Kept clean with frequent washing

Eyelash curler
Powder puffs. Washed often, as a build-up of powder stops puff
  from picking up fresh powder
Pencil sharpener
Tweezers
Miniature eyebrow brush
Lipstick brush

Make-up I can't live without

Eyeliner pencils
Powder eyeshadows
Mascara
Lipgloss
Blushers
Moisturizer
Liquid foundation
Cover-up stick

What does everyone who sees you have to look at? Your face of
course, so make it as worthwhile as possible for them. The first
contact is always visual, and what counts is the close-up. Do your
make-up to look your best at two feet, anyone twenty feet away
has to get closer if they want to know the real you.

Make up only one side of your face at a time; try different
colours and shading on each side so that you can see the effect.
It's astonishing how quickly your eye will see what works and
what doesn't. It used to be that good make-up was a professional
art, but anyone can learn the tricks of the beauty trade.

Your face is scrubbed clean; your hair pulled back; you're
ready to study your face in the mirror.

1 Cover first the right side of your face with a piece of paper;
then the left. Everyone has a 'Best' side, where the curve of
the lips and brow are just a bit prettier, the eye a better
shape. Decide which is your better side.
2 Your objective is to even up your face.
3 Make up the best eye first; correct it until it is perfect.
Then do the other to match it.

Eye Make-up

Your eyes are the most important feature of your entire body. They are the very first thing we look at in a person, and are truly the 'window to the soul'. Whatever their shape and size, ten minutes work can create the illusion that you have beautiful, alert eyes.

I grew up in the shadow of my younger sister, who had enormous brown eyes, and they were fringed with a dense jungle of lashes. Lucky her, poor me. I had little eyes which provokingly changed colour depending on what I was wearing, and thin spiky lashes. The only time they were special was after I'd been punished, or had a tantrum and cried, because tears turn them a brilliant emerald green.

At *Glamour*, the Beauty Editor Amy Greene taught me how to use eye make-up and my face was transformed. Ask anyone today my best feature and I'm sure they'd say 'enormous eyes'. Most often grey, they still look more blue or green depending on what colour is nearby, but all my efforts go into creating the effect of size and shape, rather than colour.

Fashions in make-up change a great deal more often than fashions in clothes. Eight years ago eyeliner was mandatory; six years ago false eyelashes a necessity; three years later sweeps of bold colour a must. Today my look is much more subtle; I do much less, but I think the effect is greater.

Wash your face, put on moisturizer and work on your eyes while your face is still bare. I've never understood instructions to put foundation on first; it's sure to get messed up and smudged while I work on my eyes.

Never use eye make-up removal cream or baby oil just before planning to redo your eyes. However carefully you wash, a faint film of oil will stay on your skin and lashes for hours, and no other make-up will adhere.

1 Use an erase stick, or foundation, and put a thin layer over the entire eye area; going in close to the lash base line, up to the bottom of your brows, from the side of the nose, out a quarter of an inch beyond the outside corner of the eye. Then powder the entire area with translucent powder. Now

your skin is set, and this base absorbs make-up so that it doesn't streak or change colour.

2 A few years ago most women wore a heavy slash of eyeliner but now it looks too hard. I put a series of dots, quite close together, at the base of the upper lashes. If my eyes look tired, puffy and washed out, I draw a very thin line from the inside corner on the thin ridge of flesh which lies at the base of the lashes. To get at it easily; lay your forefinger along the crease of the eye socket, and lift up the skin of the eyelid. I don't like liquid eyeliner as it's too hard to control. I prefer either a very soft pencil or a cake liner which I can make as thin or thick as I need, and with the cake I use a very tiny, skinny brush.

I then draw a dotted line underneath the bottom lashes; following the shape of my eyes until I get to the outer edge, and then (beauty expert Barbara Daly taught me this trick) I smudge the colour in a thicker, straight line, to broaden and square off the eye, making it look twice as large.

Use a soft grey or brown colour for eyeliner, but never black. At night, when I want to use more colour, I go along this bottom line with a dark green or blue pencil or powder shadow which I apply with a small sponge applicator. I also pull the applicator up at the corner and blend the colour into the eye socket. This line adds at least a quarter of an inch to the size of your eyes.

Every cosmetic company produces eye pencils but there is a great diversity in their hardness. The softer ones are better because they don't pull the thin delicate skin around the eye area so much. I have some very good skinny ones from Princess Galitzine which I keep moderately sharp with a pencil sharpener.

If you hold the pencil at a slight slant, it won't pull as much as if you hold it straight on. If you're stuck with too hard a pencil, clutch your hand till it's hot; then hold the pencil in the hollow till it's softened by your body heat.

At other times I copy a trick I learned from American fashion designer Princess Diane von Furstenberg when I did an interview with her on Capital Radio. Draw either a light blue or white line along the narrow ridge of flesh on the inside of the lower lid. If you are tired, this helps your eyes look more alive by reflecting against the whites of your eyes. Hold your bottom lid taut, slightly pulled down. Use a soft pencil and gently stroke it across from corner to corner. Careful, it tickles.

Eye shadows come in different forms: creams, liquids, powders and pencils. I always end up with a sponge applicator and a powder because they're so much easier to work with, and it's easy to rub away the colour if you make a mistake. The powder adheres to the skin, and it doesn't flake and fall into your eyes and on to your cheeks. Powder shadows are also less likely to run and streak into the crease of your eyes.

I don't think there's really much difference between the top end of the market and the chain store quality, except as to the colour choice. I like very soft subtle shades, achieving intensity through depth instead of brightness. It is usually the high fashion companies that offer the subtle tones, at least when they first become fashionable.

There's no law that says you can't blend powders and cream shadows together, but the trick is to stay within the same colour family. Watch and be aware of the matt and shine effects you are creating.

You can't collect too many different shades of shadow; fashions change, and the look you want changes, but this doesn't mean you have to buy a dozen new kits every year, just save them and look after them well. Regularly wash the applicator or brush, and throw away any crumbly bits of pressed powder.

If I want to experiment with a new shade, I'm often able to blend two old shades to see if I like the effect before I invest in a new colour. Whatever colour I'm in the mood for, I use a subdued shade, never anything brilliantly bright.

I recently discovered I could make my eyelid look much larger and deeper by covering it with a light colour, which I always used to stay away from, but I never use a frosted shade or it makes my eyes look bulging.

To contour, have three shades of any colour: use the lightest on the inside corner of the lid, a slightly darker colour over the eyeball, and the darkest at the outside, which you then round out with the sponge applicator, arching it in a downward arch along the line of the eye socket. Be sure the three colours are subtly blended into one another.

If your eyes are too far apart, use the darkest colour at the inside corner of the eye and blend out, working towards the lightest shade at the outside corner.

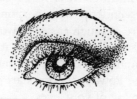

Eye make-up
Contouring with three shades of any colour plus brown line in socket

However many changes there are in eye make-up fashion, one hard and fast rule is that your eye shadow has nothing to do with the colour of your eyes, but with the colour of your clothes. Any blue shadow will be brighter than blue eyes, and the same is true of brown or green, so all you're doing is swamping your own natural colouring. Instead choose greys, browns, taupes, peaches and flesh colours that highlight your irises.

After the eyelid is coloured, I lightly pencil a brown line to contour the depth of the eye socket. This is also a trick I like doing if I'm not wearing any eye shadow at all, as it gives a feeling of space and depth to the entire area. If you have slightly bulging eyes, this is an especially good way to equalize the two areas of skin between eyelashes and brow. Use either grey or brown, only in the eye crease, and just a light natural coloured shadow on the lid. Be sure it's a matt finish to flatten the bulging even more.

I always keep my shadow within the eye socket, but this may not suit your eye shape. Experiment until you find what looks best for you. During the day I leave the area between socket and brow alone except for a light dusting of powder; but at night I use a light frosted shade such as peach or gold very lightly, and I extend it out to fill in the skin on the end of the brow bone.

If you have puffy eyelids, or a small flap of skin above the eye socket, be sure to use a dark shadow in the crease, and feather the colour into the puffiness so that it looks like a shadow. Use a powder so that it absorbs any light that hits the area and doesn't reflect it.

In the winter when I'm dead pale, I accentuate this by framing the eyes with deeper, darker shades. When I'm tanned and freckled from the sun, I often use a very pale blue pencil so that my eyes are light and reflective against my darker skin.

I don't ever use Kohl as an eyeliner because I find it fiddly, the stick applicator is unwieldy, and it gives a harsh and ageing effect.

Eyelash Curlers

Every woman in the world should be issued with an eyelash curler by the United Nations; that's how important a beauty aid I think it is. It creates a fabulous eye opening effect, only takes fifteen seconds, doesn't wear out, and makes your natural eyelashes look twice as thick.

Heavily powder your eyelashes from underneath to act as a base. Slide the curler all the way down your lashes. It is shaped to fit the eye, doesn't hurt, and won't pull out the lashes. Press and hold while you count to a slow five. Repeat this three times without moving the curler. Check the effect in the mirror and then use it again, but this time hold it nearer the edge of the lashes. Don't worry if they look very curled up, the weight of mascara straightens them out a little. Repeat process on your other eye.

Mascara

No one in the entire world ever sees me without mascara. I wear it in bed, swimming, when I'm sick, weeding, riding or just going to the corner store. The only thing I have ever discovered that dissolves waterproof mascara is tears, and so there's much less temptation to create tearful scenes; which has greatly comforted a certain number of attentive swains.

I never remove my mascara at night; and, no, I've never had an eye infection, had my eyelashes drop out, or ruined the pillow cases. I like very heavy, thick-looking lashes, and I discovered that if I started from scratch every morning, the removal oil acted as a deterrent to a heavy build-up and I never got a good enough base.

I use either Estée Lauder or Clinique black mascara. Any brand mascara is thinner when you start a new applicator, and it thickens with time. I usually have two going at once; the older wand is the first two or three coats because it is thicker, and then I break in a new one by concentrating on the outer tips and the lower lashes.

On the upper lashes I apply it from underneath, and I go all the way along the length of the lashes to the very root. This creates such a dark effect at the base that I can often omit my eyeliner dots.

Be sure there is still powder on your lashes after having curled them, and that they're bone dry or the mascara won't take. Having put on one coat I move on to the other eye so that it has time to dry before I start again. Over five minutes I probably put on six or seven coats, depending on how much there was on already. Mascara is lost in the daily wear and tear of blinking thousands of times, so it doesn't ever build up as thick as cement.

Don't let the lashes get stuck together, or they'll just look spiky, and not thick and lustrous. Either separate them with the tip of the wand, or with a tooth pick. Keep going with the mascara until they look like a garden hedge, and see what a difference the thickness framing your eyes makes to your entire face.

Then do the lower lashes, but this time applying the mascara from on top. I often see women who don't bother colouring their lower lashes, but why? Hairs grow both top and bottom; why accentuate one and not the other? I see lashes as a picture frame, and half isn't good enough.

Only practice will teach you how much to tilt your head, and what angle to hold the wand. There's always more of a mascara build-up on the tip of the applicator, but holding it horizontally separates and coats all the lashes. I find I'm using it both ways before I'm finished. Don't just settle for long looking lashes when you can have thick ones as well. On the bottom lashes it's much easier to work with the applicator tip alone.

If you've got pale skin and fair hair, brown mascara is more subtle; if you're dark, use black. I hate any other colours. Have you ever met anyone born with purple lashes?

If I'm in a mad rush, I powder the eye area, put on mascara, and that's it. Otherwise it's all done in about ten minutes and it's time well spent. I get through a mascara wand a month, and as it begins to run out, it gets so clumpy that you lose a lot of freedom in applying it, so it's one of the few products you shouldn't use to the very last drop.

I say I don't take off my mascara every night, but that doesn't mean I don't carefully clean the entire area. If you're feeling poor, put baby oil on the tip of your finger, get into the crevices of skin, rub the lid, and then carefully tissue it all off. When I'm feeling flush, I use Clinique Extremely Gentle Eye Make-up Remover. Ordinary make-up removal creams can get into your eyes, sting and smart, so be careful. If your eyes are tired, or buffeted by the weather, use eyedrops to refresh them. Be sure you get any oil off the eye area. It's very rich, and if left on, your eyes may get puffy; mine do.

Eyelash Dyeing

I once had my eyelashes dyed black before I went on holiday. This must be done professionally. I had it done at Harrods, but most big beauty salons offer it. Yes, it makes the lashes blacker for about a month; no, it doesn't make them any thicker. That's the only reason I'm sticking to mascara. I think anyone with fair hair and pale lashes should have it done automatically. The albino look is never flattering.

It must be done by a professional, not because it's dangerous, but because it's such a delicate job. If any dye gets on your skin you'll be marked, and it's pretty hard to balance brush, dye pot, hand mirror, and keep your lashes steady and unblinking if you're doing it yourself.

False Eyelashes

There was a time, in the sixties, when no fashion-conscious woman went out without her false eyelashes. If I remember right, it was also about the time I'd walk down Fifth Avenue and ten inches of thighs showed on everyone; now I shudder at the thought.

Today I think you should only wear false lashes to add thickness; and the best way to do that is by cutting off tiny clumps and applying them at intervals among your own lashes. This also solves the problem of making them look natural, and getting the long strip to sit just at the base of the lashes.

1 Since you're cutting them up, you can buy inexpensive lashes, but make sure that the texture looks reasonably real. Lift one strip out of the box with your fingers, and with your sharpest, smallest scissors cut about a third off the length; meaning from back to front, because all brands are much too long.

Now you will see that the 'hairs' are attached in tiny clumps to a rubber strip. Cut in between the little clumps till you have about six tiny bunches, each will probably have four or five hairs in it. I find it easiest to lay a tissue on my dressing-table top and let the clumps fall on to this.

2 Powder and curl your own lashes, and then apply a couple of coats of mascara, and let them dry thoroughly. Now pick up one of the tiny clumps with your tweezer so that it's held almost at the very end. Open your tube of adhesive and gently press till a tiny blob comes out on the tip. I never found any glue in an eyelash kit as good as Maybelline Eyelash Adhesive, and I always use that. Wait a couple of seconds so that the air just begins to make the adhesive sticky, and then gently touch the base of the lashes to the blob of glue until it is coated; now wait for about five seconds, and then with your other hand, pull the skin of your eyelid very taut so that you can stick the eyelash in among your own.

You must get the clump all the way down into the roots, working from above. Once it's where you want it, open your eye wide, and with your thumb and forefinger gently press together the false lash and your own lashes closest to it. Continue this process with four or five more clumps. If any adhere before they're perfectly positioned, just pull them off, clean off the adhesive, and start again. When they're all in place, apply another thick coat of mascara so you can't tell the difference between the false eyelashes and your own. Repeat the process on your other eye.

You can use the clump method on the lower lid as well, applying them from underneath your own lashes, but I think the only time to bother with this is for a close-up glamorous photograph. Otherwise, settle for lots of mascara.

Each false hair should be a slightly different length from the one next to it, just like your own lashes. If by any chance you put on a clump, and it's too long, pull it off before you trim it. I was too lazy once, didn't, and cut off a big clump of my own as well. It took weeks for them to grow back.

I never use these clumps a second time, since the tiny bits are too difficult to wash, so throw them away and cut yourself some more.

If you continuously wear false lashes be sure you have them on when you shop for glasses because, even trimmed, they may be long enough to brush against the lens, and that's annoying and uncomfortable.

My honest opinion is that if you put on as much mascara as I do, you don't need, as Estée Lauder prefers to call them, supplementary lashes. It is an additional cost in your beauty budget; they do take time; they occasionally fall off; and I like to think that what people see is all me, even if in some places there's too much of it.

Eyebrows

To test your eyebrow shape: hold a pencil vertically from nose to brow; this shows where the inner corner ideally begins. The pencil held diagonally from the outer eye corner to the nose shows the place where the outer edge of the brow should end.

1 Eyebrows that grow in heavy towards the eye close in the whole area. Pluck the space between the eye and brow, and open up the eye, making it seem larger, and giving yourself more space in which to shadow.

2 Eyebrows are a multitude of tiny hairs, all growing in the same direction. With today's natural look, it's not necessary to use any eyebrow pencil, but if you want to, then pencil in tiny little lines so it looks natural.

3 A brown eyebrow pencil looks the most natural, but if it's an emergency, use a soft Number 2 lead pencil. Be sure the point is sharp so that you get better control and less smudges.

4 Leave your eyebrows their natural shape and don't go against nature. Natural arches; rounded or straight across;

all are fine. The point of plucking is only to keep them neat and tidy.

5   I have a tiny eyebrow brush which is probably twenty-five years old; I think I may even have inherited it from my mother. That, and tweezers, are my only equipment. After finishing my make-up I brush my eyebrows to neaten up the natural arch, and then, because my fringe is so long that it pushes the eyebrow hairs downwards, I go across them once with my lipgloss, and it lubricates them just enough to keep in place.

6   By a quirk of nature, my brows are completely different shapes. I do the left one first because I like it better, and then I match the right one to it as closely as possible.

7   Check your brows every night and clean up the stragglers. Much neater, I think, than making it a weekly project and waiting for a heavier growth. For me, regrowth is from a week to ten days.

8   To Pluck Your Eyebrows:
Wash your face including the eye area.
Brush your eyebrows into the shape you want.
Hold an ice cube to the area for a minute to numb it.
Always use a magnifying mirror so that you can see the
      direction the hairs are growing in more easily.
Stretch the skin with your forefinger, always pull in the
      direction the hair grows, and only pull one hair at a time.
If there are scraggly hairs on top of your eyebrows, go right
      ahead and pull them as well.
When you've finished the first brow, do the second one to
      match. At the end, rub in a rich nourishing cream.
Never pluck before you go out, as the area will stay slightly
      red for an hour or two.

9   If you dye your hair a radically different colour, consult your hairdresser about lightening or darkening your eyebrows to blend in. This tiny trick will make your new hair colour look a lot more natural.

10   Never dye your eyebrows yourself. Firstly, you're working too close to the eye area for it to be safe; and secondly, split-second timing is all important when working with chemicals, so leave it to the professionals.

Foundation

Exactly what its name says: the base that serves as a background for everything else you put on your face. Its real purpose is to even out all the skin tones and camouflage any imperfections. You want the thinnest possible texture and this is even more true as you get older, because it sinks into every line and crevice on your face and accentuates them.

There are only four basic skin tones: yellow, pink, peach and ivory. First decide whether your skin is light, medium or dark toned; and then which of the colour families it fits. I don't want any colour from my foundation; I'll get that from my blusher/shader, and as my skin is naturally very white I choose a pale ivory tone.

If you choose the palest colour, in a shade that matches your skin, it's nearly impossible to make a bad mistake. It's only when you go to something bright that it can look glaringly wrong. Remember, you don't want to hear, 'what a terrific foundation', the compliments should be on your beautiful skin.

Foundation is one of those things you must get expert advice on. All the big cosmetic houses have different formulas in their lines, and it's hard to know which is best for you. And do you remember that old wives' tale about testing foundation on the back of your hand? Well, it's looney. The skin tones on your face and the back of your hand have nothing to do with each other. Test where you're going to use it, your face.

If you've got a spotty, troubled skin, choose one of the medicated products on the market which may do some good while it's covering up the damage.

On my splotchy skin I use a very light-weight, oil-free, foundation, Pore Minimizer Make-up by Clinique. It's very thin, and on the clear parts of my face, one coat does it. Where I need more coverage I just add another coat when the first one is dry. It's the most long lasting cover I've found, and if after three or four hours the central T zone is looking too shiny, I use a tissue to blot, and then a light dab of powder.

1 Wash, moisturize, and leave for ten minutes while it's absorbed. Lightly blot with a tissue and then put on your

foundation. Anything liquid is lighter textured and easier to blend. Apply a very thin film with clean finger tips. Start with a dab on the upper part of your cheek and work it down towards your chin. Work it around your ear, and stop just short of the hairline. The reason for working down, the opposite of when you cleanse, is that you want make-up to stay on the surface of your skin for a smooth, lustrous finish. If you work up, it sinks into the pores and gets absorbed.

2 Cover one side before starting the other so that you are blending while the liquid is at its wettest. Despite what we learned at our mother's knee, don't carry your foundation all the way down your neck. Not only is the skin texture different but you'll get make-up on all your clothes. I just curve my fingers around the chin and jaw curve and blend it in there.

3 Instead of a cover stick, I use Clinique's Continuous Coverage, a cream foundation in a tube, under my eyes, around my nostrils, and to cover any problem spot. The most important thing is to use as little as possible. Your own skin texture shows through whatever product you choose and, Honest Injun, just because you use a heavy oil-based foundation, it doesn't mean you'll have any better coverage.

The most important trick I ever learned was how to work the principles of light and dark, shine and matt, to create illusions. Wherever there's shine it brings the area forward, powder it for a matt finish and it recedes back. Now I powder the tip of my nose, under my eyes and on my chin. The rest I leave shiny.

Anything pale, shiny or frosted is a highlight. The area you use it on stands out. A powdery matt finish in any smoky, subtle colour is a low light, and adds depth to your face. Both work, both are necessary, but in different places. Only practice and close examination in your mirror will tell you which you want where.

I don't try lots of tricks with coloured lines and carefully blended shadings; it just looks contrived on me. But I do try to conceal the lines around my mouth. As the wrinkle becomes a yawning crevice, the skin on either side stops the light from getting into the area. To correct, get the lightest shade concealing stick and draw a light line from the corner of your mouth to the corner of your nose. The increased lightness will give the illusion of lifting your entire face. It's a fantastic phony face lift. Try it and see if I'm not right.

One small tip I recently learned: heat means penetration; so don't put on your foundation when you go to the hairdresser. Sitting under the drier will make all your pores open and the foundation will sink right in. Apply it after your hair is done.

Since I got my heavy fringe I've stopped putting any foundation on my forehead.

Blushers

When I was sixteen it was called rouge, and the trick was to use it so that no one could tell you wore any. Today the same product is called all sorts of things: shapers, contour stick, shader and blusher. They come in creams, liquids or powders; I use powder and a brush because I find that the easiest to blend.

Use your colour with a sure hand to create the chiselled effect of high cheekbones. It's not difficult to know where to put it. With the side of your thumb, press down into your cheek so you can feel the bone. Colour in just under the bone, and bring the colour out towards your temple, on an upwards slant. To add a little highlight, run your concealing stick along the plane of the cheek-bone so that light reflects off it.

Article after article is written about all the wonderful things you can do with shading to give your face shadows and dimensions, but however hard I practised I just looked as if I had a dirty face. So, that put paid to that, which goes to prove that you can have everything, but everything won't work.

I have half a dozen powder blushers; some tawny, others pink, the latest one more plum. Which one I choose depends on what colour is on my eyes, and what I'm going to wear. It's as simple as that.

Barbara Daly taught me more tricks for photography:

1   To create beautiful cheek hollows; apply dark brown shadow underneath the blusher you've placed on the cheek-

bone. Use a powder so it's a matt shadow, and your skin there will recede even further into the shadow of the high-lighted cheekbone.

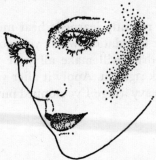

Trick 1. Beautiful cheek hollows

2 For an instant face lift, start your blusher directly under the outside edge of your iris. Brush the colour along the bone and out to the temple; then create a V shape by bringing the brush back towards the centre of your forehead, about half an inch above the brow. This 'V' draws the attention to the upper part of your face and creates an uplifted look.

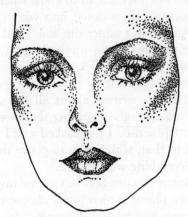

Trick 2. Instant face lift

3 If you have a large nose, don't get blusher too far in on the cheek, or it will only draw attention to it.
4 Don't bring blusher in too close under your eyes, or it will make them look small.

5   If you're more interested in contouring than you are in giving your face colour, go for the browny shades.

Powder

As you get older, what keeps your skin looking young and dewy is moisture, so it's self-defeating to cover that which you've got naturally. Lightly dust your nose and any problem spots with translucent powder, but leave the rest of your face naturally shiny. Apply with a clean velour puff, using a press and roll motion.

Any colour in your powder will undo anything else on your face. Translucent powder takes on whatever skin colour you have after just a few minutes. You can use a big fat brush to apply powder, but a puff gives you more control.

If you have very dry skin, try this. Wet some cotton wool with cold water and then get rid of the excess moisture. Dab it gently all over your face to set your make-up.

If your skin is excessively oily, you can lightly fluff powder all over, but by changing the look of your skin texture it accentuates your large pores, and makes your skin look years older.

Lip Colour

Lips are one feature that should look deliberately sexy, which means soft, shiny, moist, and never gooked up with a 'Don't Touch Me' colour.

If I use a lipstick I use a colourless lipgloss on top, but now glosses come in such scrumptious colours, and they give you all the advantages of colour, coverage and shine in one.

1   Always use a brush to apply an accurate outline. Fill in your cupid's bow first, then draw out to the corners of your mouth and don't stop short. Fill in the bottom lip from outer corner to the centre. To get a perfect shape, I balance my right elbow on the dressing table, manipulating the brush with my thumb and index finger.

2   If your lips are dark and wrinkled, cover them with lashings of petroleum jelly while you're at home, and be

careful when you're applying colour. Outline the shape, then fill in the colour with a brush, using downward strokes to fill in the cracks. Any frosted colour will only exaggerate wrinkles. Avoid long-staying lipsticks; use glosses, and re-apply frequently.

3 If your lipstick blurs into the tiny lines around your mouth; first apply a thin coating of foundation, then dust with powder and finish with a matt colour lipstick. Blot and reapply. Forget glosses and very creamy lipsticks.

4 To emphasize a well-shaped cupid's bow, put a dot of white in the inside of the little valley above it. Lightly blend.

5 If you have very thin lips, don't paint on a bigger shape, it shows. Just use light, bright colours to attract attention.

6 For full, wide lips, brush on a dark muted colour and gloss the top lip, but only the centre of the bottom one.

7 If your bottom lip is too big in proportion to the upper one, use a deeper colour on the lower lip, and a slightly lighter colour on the upper lip. Gloss only on the top.

8 If your lips are chapped, and lip colour cracks and flakes, wipe off completely with creamy cleanser before applying a new coat.

9 If you get a reaction to even hypo-allergenic brands, try the Beauty Without Cruelty range. Made with non-animal substances they are the solution for many women.

10 Whatever idiosyncrasies your mouth has, I'm opposed to pencil lines, deeper borders, and brighter centres. It's all just too gimmicky and phony. Not very kissable either. Would you kiss a chequer board?

The Do It Yourself Make-Over

I once heard a psychiatrist say that in order to have a successful psychoanalysis, a patient has to have a lot of energy and spirit. Now you know that's exactly what a Do It Yourself Make-Over takes as well.

12 ❧ Travelling

Travelling

I do three kinds of travelling. The easiest is the weekend in the country staying with friends: two days where I know pretty well what the form is; what I'll be doing, and what I'll need in the way of clothes.

The biggest eye-opener when I came to England was getting used to the fact that, because the calendar said June, it didn't mean I could leave my heavy cardigans and Wellingtons at home. Now, dinner dresses always have long sleeves, and I play tennis in blue jeans, and not skimpy white shorts.

Depending on my mood, I take either a skirt or pair of blue jeans, and half a dozen alternative tops; a concealing dressing gown that in the summer also goes over a bathing suit; a pair of sandals that get me down the corridor to the bath, as easily as out to the pool; lots of books, my needlepoint, sponge bag; and that's the lot. All packed in a small blue denim case that's fine half full, and expands amazingly when it needs to.

I go back to New York at least once a year; but with Freddy's blessed Sky Train running, I'd rather go twice a year for a week, now that I don't have to worry about minimum excursion stays. I used to take far too much with me, always tempted to show off my British fashions. But the light finally dawned when waving my press card didn't protect me, and I had to pay a hefty overweight charge. It also occurred to me that in two weeks of working I saw most people only once; so why not wear one smashing outfit into the ground. It might have bored me to tears, but no one else would ever know.

A skirt and coat, or suit, have been my mainstay; with lots of different shirts. Two mid-calf length dresses take me out to dinner every night, and on my longer trips I've packed one slightly more dressy outfit, just in case something big comes up. My sponge bag has the same things in it as for a weekend away. The only difference is that I take a larger quantity. Again relatively easy because it can all be pre-organized.

The third category can only be called spontaneous – and, for any unmarried female, not coming home after dinner has to be a possibility, if not a probability. If you're wearing a long, revealing evening dress, it's a great deal more practical, not to mention discreet, to get out of bed and go home while it's still dark.

But these days most of us very rarely dress for dinner in a way that would prove embarrassing if we were seen at 8 a.m. the next morning. So, allow for enough mad money to get home in case the evening turns out to be a dreadful mistake; take tiny containers of moisturizer, foundation, blusher, lipgloss, scent and a comb, and that's it.

Packing

Within a week of becoming a junior fashion editor on *Glamour*, I found myself on a plane to Boston, laden with suitcases full of clothes to photograph for a career girl story. I got to be a dab hand with the tissue paper; and that first of many trips led me to formulate certain survival tactics.

1 Take twice as much to read as there possibly seems time for. My idea of purgatory is to find myself stranded with nothing to read; I even carry a book for a ten-minute ride on a London bus.
2 Carry absolutely everything with you that you couldn't do without, if you and your luggage got separated.
3 It's not only easier to carry; but it's much easier to pack two cases neatly than one big one.
4 It takes just about as long to pack for a weekend as it does for a two-week trip. You're not taking as much, but the organization is the same.

Travelling

To Pre-Plot a Trip

1   What will the weather be like?
2   What sort of people will you be seeing, business acquaintances on whom you want to make a businesslike impression; friends whose life style is casual and relaxed?
3   How long is the travelling time?
4   What sort of transportation are you using?
5   Are you travelling alone?
6   Will you be working or playing? Are any special clothes needed for either?
7   How many different stops will you be making?
8   How long will you be away?

My Basic Survival Kit for any length trip

General Items

Alarm clock
Radio
Aspirin; Vitamins; Valium; Vitamin C
    tablets; Anti-histamine
Sewing kit with scissors
Kleenex

Safety pins
Band aids
Neutral cream shoe
    polish and applicator
    cloths
Folding umbrella

Cosmetic Kit

Moisturizer
Foundation
Blusher
Translucent powder
Eyelash curler
Eyeliner pencils
Eye shadows

Mascara
Lipstick brush
Lipgloss
Scent
Comb
Headband
Hair clips

Sponge Bag

All liquids in miniature plastic bottles collected from trial size samples over the years.

Face soap
Buf-Puf

7th Day scrub
Shampoo

Look Like A Million

Sponge	Conditioner
Bath oil	Cotton buds
Anti-perspirant	Cotton wool
Dusting powder	Nail varnish remover
Toothbrush and toothpaste	Nail varnish; base coat plus
Dental floss	whatever colour I'm using
Pumice stone	Hair drier
Emery board	Nail file
Body cream	Eye drops
Skin tonic	Tweezers

Tote Bag

Passport	Pens, pencils
Spare wallet with foreign currency	Cosmetic pouch
and traveller's cheques	Sponge bag
Books	Scarf
Diary	Jewellery case

These lists may seem ludicrously long to you: but just you wait till you find yourself twenty miles from civilization late at night and you're desperate for something safely sitting at home. I know, I've been there, and now I'm prepared for fire, famine and holocaust.

It's human nature to take too much: plan ahead and take out all the things you want. Edit them to see what goes with the most things, what can be left behind. I start by getting everything out and hanging on the door jamb three days before I'm to leave. I take either black or brown shoes and boots, never both; and so the clothing scheme evolves from that one basic decision. Having weeded out anything impractical I check to make sure they're all in perfect condition: cleaned, buttons on, hems sewn. I always travel in boots to save packing space, but I take a pair of knitted sock slippers with me for the flight. I got mine from Pan Am at least eight years ago.

Packing things tightly helps keep them neat, and leads to less wrinkling and shifting around. One case I pack with all my clothes that lie perfectly flat. To unpack, everything goes on a hanger and that's it. The second case has everything else: shoes, lingerie, accessories, hair drier, etc. They all get packed in separate fabric bags or felt shoe bags with drawstring tops. After un-packing, they get put away in drawers, still in their separate little pouches. I was staying on Grand Bahama Island a few years ago when I suddenly had to change rooms at two minutes notice; and it was just a question of seconds while I slung all my little sacks into a pillow case, clothes over my arm, and I was off down the corridor to my new home, where everything was stored away equally speedily.

If there's going to be an intermediate overnight stop, I put things I'll need right on the top while I'm packing, and that's all I take out. Clothes are going to get wrinkled in a suitcase and there's little difference whether they've been left there three hours or three days. I use tissue paper between every single garment – not to prevent wrinkles (I don't think it does) but as extra protection in case a calamity happens.

I don't believe in special clothes for different countries. It's either a hot country or a cold one; that's it.

Practice does make perfect. The more often you pack, the quicker it goes.

Clothes

It used to be very fashionable to carry one change with you in case your bags were mislaid for twenty-four hours. Waste of time, I think. What you want to wear is sure to be in the missing bag. I keep my sponge bag and cosmetic pouch in my tote bag, more to prevent spillage and breakage from rough handling: clothes I leave to fend for themselves.

In the mid-sixties, brightly printed Emilio Pucci silk jersey dresses became the cult uniform for the Beautiful People. Not only did they have a perfect pedigree, they were supposed to be the solution for comfortable travel clothing. Well, I saved up and bought one. I think it cost nearly £100, which was a huge sum ten years ago; and it was the biggest disappointment of my life. The jersey wrinkled just as much as any other fabric; the texture made me feel sticky, and the clear, light colours meant it spent as much time at the cleaners as it did on me.

Now I wear whatever I want to wear at my destination. It can always be ironed.

I pack the following:

1 coat or jacket: chosen to go over everything	nightgown
	robe
1 shawl to wear as evening wrap	shirts
	skirts
1 pair of boots	pullovers
1 pair of low-heeled walking shoes, or sandals, depending on destination	belts
	scarves
	small evening handbag
1 pair flat-heeled black silk pumps	dinner dresses
	bathing suit and tee shirts if
lingerie	destination warrants it
stockings	

Luggage

Definitely a cheap and cheerful area of expense. It may be chic to adorn yourself with Gucci and Louis Vuitton, so treat yourself to a big shoulder strap satchel or tote bag that you'll get just as much use out of when still on the ground. But it's daft to invest £200 on a suitcase that 'Fly Me' Airlines is just going to batter, bruise and bash for you.

As a journalist, there was a period when I spent as much time travelling as I did on dry land. I got myself a carpet bag satchel and one of those plastic dress bags that takes about six dresses. Whatever I could fit into those two cases came with me; otherwise it stayed at home. I carried them on and off the plane myself, never checked anything, and saved hours waiting around for a suitcase to appear.

To me, the definition of a good suitcase is one that is well constructed and doesn't fall apart on me in a crowded waiting room. Brightly coloured, lightweight canvas cases suit me perfectly. Chain stores do smashing ones; and it helps get you through the Customs green line if your clothes and cases don't look too rich. If you've got chain store luggage which is hard to recognize; tie brightly coloured yarn on the handles.

For security reasons, don't put addressed labels on the outside of your case. Instead, stick them on the inside of the lid. Accept the tag the check-in attendant always presses on you, and stuff it in a pocket.

If you have to travel light, get a duffel bag. It's easy to carry over your shoulder, and it holds so much because it accommodates the shape of what you put in it. Pack it sailor fashion, roll everything, and stuff it really tightly so that it doesn't get droopy.

Never store leather luggage in either a damp place, where it will get mildewed and have a terrible odour, or an overheated cupboard, which will dry out the leather, crack and eventually rot it.

I 3 ✿ Getting Your Act Together

Voices

The way you sound has an astonishing effect on the way people see you. Sometimes we think someone is unattractive, and don't realize that a loud, screechy, high-pitched or nasal voice so grates on our nerves that we don't like to look at a person who sounds like that.

I can't remember who said that the Americans and British are one people divided by a common language: but at one time I got very self-conscious about my speech because people love teasing me about the way I pronounce things. Of course, I thought I sounded as British as the Queen, until I started on the radio, and Michael Aspel straightened me out about that one.

A spectacular voice is one of the best beauty tricks you can learn. If your voice is really horrible, you must get help from a professional, because you have to learn how to pitch the sound and what to do about controlling your vocal chords; but everyone can improve their inflections, the raising and lowering of tonal qualities, and the loud or soft volume control.

The more musical a range you put in your voice, the more people will listen to you; and lovely Michael Aspel taught me to get attention by the tone, and not the volume, since he said no one likes being shouted at, and he was right. If you vary inflections, and try to change resonances, your voice automatically gets lower and more pleasant to listen to.

There are two easy tests to tell you what you sound like to other people. If you've got any recording machine, make a tape of yourself; try to do it for five minutes, and talking to someone else. Tape your side of a phone conversation, for instance, because you want to hear your responses to other people.

But, if you don't have access to a tape machine, go into a room, preferably small, close the door so it's sealed off, put your fingers in your ears, which creates a sound tunnel effect, and talk to yourself for a few minutes.

Is it flat and nasal, so that you sound like a whiner? A high raspy voice, pitched through your nose, sounds childish and immature. If you speak in a flat staccato manner it comes across as aggressive, abrupt and impatient, and puts people's backs up. Are you tight-jawed, speaking through clenched teeth? If so you probably sound pretentious and affected.

Correct a monotone, and put lots of expression in your voice. Choose a good book, a novel with lots of spirited dialogue. Anything by Georgette Heyer is absolutely perfect. Now read out loud to yourself fifteen minutes a day. Go ahead, really ham it up. At the end of a week, it will be automatic to speak like that in conversation. Listen to yourself, and see if I'm not right.

You may not have realized that people see you as dumb when you know you're clever: or boring when you know in your heart of hearts that you're fascinating: just because you sound that way. And please, whatever you do, don't ever say 'um' or 'er', neither one, in any circumstances, is necessary, and if you listen to yourself you'll be shocked how often it creeps in.

Check your Voice

1 Is your voice quality clear and vibrant? If you control your speech through your throat, it will sound too thin, tremulous and breathy.
2 Is the pitch just below the middle of your vocal range? Lower pitched tones allow more inflection.
3 Is the volume right?
4 What speed are you speaking at? Too rapid sounds nervous. Too slow comes across as dull. Drawling appears careless.

5 How good is your phrasing? The listener should hear thoughts, not individual words.
6 Do you stress the accent in the right place? Otherwise the listener will lose the sense of what you're saying.

Sex Appeal

Sex and beauty can't be separated, and the elixir of love may not be bottled by any cosmetic company, but it puts a sparkle in your eyes, and a glow on your skin that's there for the world to see. I've never seen any proof that regular sex in itself is particularly good exercise; it doesn't burn up more calories than a brisk walk in the fresh air; but knowing a lover will see you naked makes you more aware of your body, and you do more to stay in shape. Being loved makes me feel smug, and puts a smile on my face.

Any woman who is pleased with her face, and proud of her body, is going to be sexy. Maybe she won't have Farrah Fawcett-Major's face, or Raquel Welch's measurements, but she'll have a zest for life, and an energy that every man will find appealing.

I hope that I'll still be attractive to the man I love twenty years from now, and the Number One reason for staying attractive must be that there will still be someone who wants to go to bed with you. If you think you're not sexy; you won't be sexy. Be happy, funny and more interested in other people than in yourself, and you'll find yourself the most fancied lady in town.

Smiles

Your face looks fabulous; your hair is as shiny as satin; your body beautifully firm; your clothes show you off to perfection. Super! Now the only thing to think about is the big smile on your face.

Patrick, the wisest man I know, taught me, and he's always right, that if you smile at people, ten times out of ten, they're going to smile back. A smile makes your voice more persuasive, your face instantly prettier, and your personality warmer. Try it; and sue me if I'm wrong.

Look Like A Million

Self-Confidence

Self-confidence doesn't come easily; and you'll probably wind up with doubt about some things though not about others.

I knew long ago that I was never going to be the prettiest or the smartest girl in town. *Tant pis*; but I wasn't willing to be anything less than the very best that was in me. Looking attractive, and wearing the right clothes, makes me feel confident. Is that really so selfish? I don't think so.

When I'm happy and like myself, subconsciously, everything I do fits the picture I have of myself. When I'm in a blue funk, convinced that I'm just a great big lump, you can bet that's exactly how I look. A little self-defeating, isn't it, when just a half-hour's work in front of the mirror can make such a difference to the picture I have of myself.

Make the most of yourself. No one can ask more than that of you. Few of us are lucky enough to get a second chance at life when things go wrong, so get on with it, there isn't any time to waste.

I've been spoilt by good luck. I became a journalist by accident; and courtesy of an editor called Clay Felker: and it was only then I discovered that it gave me everything I wanted: it took me to places and introduced me to people I would not ordinarily have come into contact with. In fact, if it hadn't been for Prince Philip who agreed to give me an interview for the *Daily Mail* I would have found it nearly impossible to make my way in Fleet Street. So I have a lot to thank him for.

Self-confidence has given me the key to the door marked 'curiosity'. I can afford now to say 'why not' when exposed to something new, and it doesn't matter if it's a new hair-do, dress style, country or person. It was the old, uptight me who was afraid of everything I didn't know.

Don't settle for second best; not in yourself and not in the people close to you. There is a radiance attached to people who are happy and confident that I hope you will have. Dazzle everyone, be an asset, have an aura, set a style, like yourself, and happiness will follow.

Index

Index